CURRENT TOPICS IN

DEVELOPMENTAL BIOLOGY

VOLUME 9

CURRENT TOPICS IN
DEVELOPMENTAL BIOLOGY

EDITED BY

A. A. MOSCONA

DEPARTMENTS OF BIOLOGY AND PATHOLOGY
THE UNIVERSITY OF CHICAGO
CHICAGO, ILLINOIS

ALBERTO MONROY

C.N.R. LABORATORY OF MOLECULAR EMBRYOLOGY
ARCO FELICE (NAPLES), ITALY

VOLUME 9
Experimental Systems for Analysis
of Cell Differentiation

1975

ACADEMIC PRESS   New York • San Francisco • London

A Subsidiary of Harcourt Brace Jovanovich, Publishers

ACADEMIC PRESS, INC.
111 Fifth Avenue, New York, New York 10003

United Kingdom Edition published by
ACADEMIC PRESS, INC. (LONDON) LTD.
24/28 Oval Road, London NW1

LIBRARY OF CONGRESS CATALOG CARD NUMBER: 66-28604

ISBN 0–12–153109–0

PRINTED IN THE UNITED STATES OF AMERICA

CONTENTS

CHAPTER 1. **Histones, Chromatin Structure, and Control of Cell Division**

E. M. BRADBURY

CHAPTER 2. **Control of Gene Expression during the Terminal Differentiation of Erythroid Cells**

A. FANTONI, M. LUNADEI, AND E. ULLU

CHAPTER 3. **Changing Populations of Reiterated DNA Transcripts during Early Echinoderm Development**

H. R. WHITELEY AND A. H. WHITELEY

CHAPTER 4. **Regulation of Messenger RNA Translation during Insect Development**

JOSEPH ILAN AND JUDITH ILAN

CHAPTER 5. **Chemical and Structural Changes within Chick Erythrocyte Nuclei Introduced into Mammalian Cells by Cell Fusion**

R. APPELS AND NILS R. RINGERTZ

CHAPTER 6. ***Drosophila* Antigens: Their Spatial and Temporal Distribution, Their Function and Control**

DAVID B. ROBERTS

LIST OF CONTRIBUTORS

Numbers in parentheses indicate the pages on which the authors' contributions begin.

R. APPELS,* *Institute for Medical Cell Research and Genetics, Medical Nobel Institute, Karolinska Institutet, Stockholm, Sweden* (137)

E. M. BRADBURY, *Biophysics Laboratory, Physics Department, Portsmouth Polytechnic, Portsmouth, United Kingdom* (1)

A. FANTONI, *Laboratorio di Radiobiologia Animale, C.S.N. Casaccia, CNEN, Roma, Italy* (15)

JOSEPH ILAN, *Department of Anatomy and Developmental Biology Center, School of Medicine, Case Western Reserve University, Cleveland, Ohio* (89)

JUDITH ILAN, *Department of Anatomy and Developmental Biology Center, School of Medicine, Case Western Reserve University, Cleveland, Ohio* (89)

M. LUNADEI, *II Cattedra di Biologia Generale, Università di Roma, Policlinico Umberto I, Roma, Italy* (15)

NILS R. RINGERTZ, *Institute for Medical Cell Research and Genetics, Medical Nobel Institute, Karolinska Institutet, Stockholm, Sweden* (137)

DAVID B. ROBERTS, *Genetics Laboratory, Biochemistry Department, Oxford University, Oxford, England* (167)

E. ULLU, *II Cattedra di Biologia Generale, Università di Roma, Policlinico Umberto I, Roma, Italy* (15)

A. H. WHITELEY, *Departments of Microbiology and Zoology and the Friday Harbor Laboratories, University of Washington, Seattle, Washington* (39)

H. R. WHITELEY, *Departments of Microbiology and Zoology and the Friday Harbor Laboratories, University of Washington, Seattle, Washington* (39)

* Present address: Division of Plant Industry, CSIRO, P. O. Box 1600, Canberra, A.C.T., Australia.

PREFACE

It has been pointed out to the Editors that the publication of the tenth volume in this series represents an important and happy occasion worthy of special notice. While we deeply appreciate this expression of encouragement, and are gratified by the acceptance and usefulness of this publication, we also wonder if the metric system has not unduly conditioned all of us to assign a special importance to decimal repeats. We have looked upon each one of the previous volumes as a significant and special contribution to the literature in Developmental Biology. Frankly, keeping up with the rapid progress in this field has been more to our liking than celebrating past accomplishments. Perhaps significantly, Volumes 9 and 10 appear almost simultaneously, endeavoring to catch up with some of the exciting and important current research in the field of development and differentiation.

We wish to thank the contributors to Volumes 9 and 10 for meeting the aims, standards and deadlines of *Current Topics in Developmental Biology*. We also thank the staff of Academic Press for their efforts and cooperation.

A. A. MOSCONA
ALBERTO MONROY

CONTENTS OF PREVIOUS VOLUMES

CHAPTER 1

HISTONES, CHROMATIN STRUCTURE, AND CONTROL OF CELL DIVISION

E. M. Bradbury

BIOPHYSICS LABORATORY, PHYSICS DEPARTMENT
PORTSMOUTH POLYTECHNIC
PORTSMOUTH, UNITED KINGDOM

I. Introduction

During the past twelve months new proposals have been made concerning the molecular structure of the basic subunit of the eukaryotic chromosome and control of cell division. These proposals are interrelated and involve the properties and functions of the histones, which for many years have been an enigma. Because of their close association with DNA, histones have been implicated in many aspects of both the structure and the control of the functions of chromosomes. Now it is becoming increasingly clear that one important function of histones is in the maintenance and control of the structure of the chromosomes through the cell cycle.

II. Histones

Histones fall into five classes; the very lysine-rich histone H1 (F1, 1), intermediate histones H2A (F2A2 and I1b2) and H2B (F2B, I1b1), and the arginine-rich histone H3 (F3, III) and H4 (F2A1, IV). These five histones are found in almost all higher organisms; a notable exception is avian erythrocytes, where histone H1 is largely replaced by another very lysine-rich histone H5 (F2C, V) (Neelin, 1964). A major contribution to the understanding of histones has come from the determination of their sequence (Croft, 1973). From the sequences, two important properties have emerged; first, except for H1, histones of the same class from different higher organisms are very similar. In particular the sequence for histone H4 is rigidly conserved, with a mutation rate of 0.06 mutation per 100 residues per 10^8 years (DeLange *et al.*, 1969a,b);

this implies that each and every residue in these proteins is involved in interactions required for their functions. Histone H3 exhibits a similar high degree of sequence conservation (DeLange, 1974). Second, the distribution of residues in the histone sequences are highly asymmetric, giving rise to well-defined segments of quite different characteristics. Thus the amino terminal segments comprising one-quarter to one-third of the molecules of histones H2A, H2B, H3, and H4 are strongly basic and also contain a high proportion of the helix destabilizing residues proline, glycine, and serine; in addition, the short segments at the carboxyl ends of histone H2A and H2B are also basic. The regions complementary to these basic segments, i.e., the central regions of H2A and H2B and the carboxyl region H3 and H4 are apolar and contain most of the potential of the histone polypeptide chain for helix formation (Lewis and Bradbury, 1974). Histone H1 differs from the other four histones in that carboxyl half of the molecule is strongly basic, the central segment 41 to 107 contains almost all the apolar residues while the amino segment 1–14 is acidic and 15–35 is strongly basic (Jones *et al.*, 1974).

Isolated histones in aqueous solution are largely in the random coil conformation. Addition of salt, however, induces a conformational change in all the histones and self-aggregation in all the histones except H1. High-resolution nuclear magnetic resonance (NMR) and optical spectroscopic studies of these changes show that the apolar regions are involved both in the conformational changes and in histone–histone interactions while the basic ends of the histones retain the high mobility of the random coil conformation (see references in Bradbury *et al.*, 1973a). Further, on looking at the interactions of the histones with DNA it has been found that the basic segments are the primary sites of interaction with DNA. The general picture is therefore emerging that the apolar regions of the histones H2A, H2B, H3, and H4 can take up specific conformations which are the sites for histone–histone interactions while the basic segments are the primary sites for interaction with DNA. Studies of the properties of large fragments of histone molecules obtained by cleavage at a small number of sites support this general picture (Lewis *et al.*, 1974).

III. Cross Interactions of Histones

In most higher organisms the histone to DNA ratio is approximately unity and histones are present in almost equal molar amounts, except for the very lysine-rich histone H1, which is almost twice as large as the other histones. The possibility exists, therefore, that histones H2A, H2B, H3, and H4 could be present in equal stoichiometric ratios. A statistical analysis (E. M. Bradbury and H. R. Matthews, unpublished) of all data on the quantitative amount of histones in a wide range of tissues indicates that this stoichiometry holds for histones H3 and H4 but the amounts of H2A and H2B are more variable. It is clear that additional quantitative estimates of histones are required in a wide range of tissues. There is physicochemical evidence for specific cross interaction between pairs of histones (D'Anna and Isenberg, 1973; Isenberg, 1974). Additional evidence for histone complexes in total histone came from var der Westhuyzen and von Holt (1971), who attempted to separate histones on Sephadex G-100 and found two peaks; H1 ran together with H3, and H4 and H2A together with H2B. Kornberg and Thomas (1974) cross-linked histones in the complexes of H3 and H4 with dimethyl suberimidate and found evidence for tetramers of H3 and H4, i.e., $(H3)_2(H4)_2$. NMR studies of these complexes are in progress, although it is expected that the cross interactions of histones will involve the structural apolar regions found in the self-interactions of histones, leaving the basic segments free to interact with DNA. In all these studies, there is no evidence that histones H1 takes part in interactions with other histones.

IV. Basic Structural Unit of Chromatin

The observations of a series of rings at ca. 11.0, 5.5, 3.7, 2.7, and 2.2 nm in the X-ray patterns of native and reconstituted chromatin indicates the existence of a fundamental structural repeat. In 1964 M. H. F. Wilkins proposed a model of a uniform supercoil with a pitch of 12.0 nm and an outer diameter of 13.0 nm to explain this characteristic X-ray pattern, and it should be noted that in the model calculations (Pardon and Wilkins 1972) only the X-ray scatter from the DNA component was considered. On this model therefore, the 11.0 nm ring comes from the basic spacing of the DNA in the supercoil while the other rings are higher orders of this repeat. Another more irregular supercoil with pitch varying between 4.5 and 7.0 nm and an outer diameter of 8.0–12.0 nm has been proposed by Bram and Ris (1971). In these models, the DNA forms the backbone of the structure and is complexed with histones in an unspecified manner. A "particles on a string" model has recently been suggested by Olins and Olins (1973, 1974) from electron microscope studies of nuclei swollen in water in which they observed "linear arrays of spherical chromatin particle." Woodcock (1973) has made similar observations.

The possibility of globularity in chromatin was first suggested by Bram and Ris (1971). From physicochemical studies of the products of limited nuclease digestion of chromatin, van Holde and co-workers (Rill and van Holde, 1973; Sahasrabuddhe and van Holde, 1974) have also found evidence for a globular subunit structure in chromatin. Further, Hewish and Burgoyne (1973) have found that endonuclease digestion of chromatin in rat liver nuclei gave DNA places in integral units of about 200 base pairs (see ref. 9 in Kornberg, 1974); they suggested that this was evidence for a fundamental regularity in the distribution of proteins in the chromatin structure. [This observation has been confirmed by Noll (1974), who found a basic DBA subunit of 205 base pairs after nuclease digestion and a second subunit of 170 base pairs.] Using these observations, Kornberg (1974) proposed that each 200-pair unit is associated with a tetramer of histones $(H3)_2$ $(H4)_2$ and two each of the histones H2A and H2B to give a subunit of chromatin. It is quite clear that additional structural data are required to obtain a low resolution of the basic structure of the chromosome and to distinguish between the various models preposed. In particular, information is required on the relative disposition of the protein and DNA components of chromation. Neutron techniques are particularly suited for this type of study and have the potential to distinguish between the scatter of the protein and DNA components of chromatin (Moore et al., 1974; Stuhrmann, 1974).

V. Neutron Diffraction of Chromatin

Probably the most important reason why neutron techniques have particular application to studies of protein/nucleic acid complexes comes from the very large difference between the neutron atomic scattering factors for hydrogen and deuterium. As a result of this, the difference of the average neutron scatter of H_2O (-0.06×10^{-12} cm) compared to D_2O ($+0.63 \times 10^{-12}$ cm) is so large that it allows the scattering from all biological molecules to be matched simply by adding a mixture of H_2O and D_2O in the proportions required to give the same neutron scatter as the biological molecule. This can be illustrated by considering the components of chromatin. The average scatter of histone can be computed to be 0.14×10^{-12} cm and for DNA, 0.30×10^{-12} cm; the mixtures of H_2O and D_2O to match these neutron scatter factors are 38% D_2O/62% H_2O for the histones and 64% D_2O/36% H_2O for DNA. These D_2O values are widely separated and enable an estimate to be made of the individual contributions of the protein and the DNA to the total scatter of chromatin (Baldwin et al., 1975).

This approach allows a very gentle method, simply by recording the neutron scatter patterns of chromatin in different mixtures of H_2O and D_2O, to obtain information on the relative disposition of the protein and DNA components. Thus for the Wilkins supercoil model it would be expected that the whole series of low-angle rings which are attributed to the regularity of the coiling of the DNA would be observed at the D_2O/H_2O ratio that matches the protein scatter and, in contrast, would be greatly weakened at the ratio that matches the DNA scatter. The neutron results do not accord with the Wilkins supercoil model. It was found that the low-angle rings at ca. 11.0, 5.5, 3.7, and 2.7 nm originated not from the spacing of a single structural repeat and its higher orders as assumed in the proposal of a regular supercoil, but from different spatial arrangements of the histones and DNA (Baldwin et al., 1975). Histones H2A, H2B, H3, and H4 are arranged so that they contribute a broad distribution of neutron scatter, which is strong in the region of the 11.0 nm peak and also has a strong component at 3.7 nm while the DNA component contributes to the rings at 5.5 and 2.7 nm. Further observations of the behavior of the neutron scatter with changes in the H_2O/D_2O ratios suggest that the mean radius of the DNA is larger than for the complex of the four histones H2A, H2B, H3, and H4. It should be noted at this stage that there are data from X-ray studies of chromatin depleted in the very lysine-rich histone H1 to show that this histone is not involved in the structure giving rise to the low-angle diffraction pattern (Bradbury et al., 1972), but that the other four histones are involved. Further, measurements of the radius of gyration of chromatin and H1-depleted chromatin indicate that the H1 histone is on the outside of the complex (Bram et al., 1974).

We consider the globular "particles on a string" model and propose that each subunit consists of a core of interacting apolar segments of the histones H2A, H2B, H3, and H4 surrounded by DNA partially complexed with the extended basic segments of the histones. Such interactions are in keeping with the properties of the histones described earlier. The globular subunits may contain the tetramer $(H3)_2(H4)_2$ found in salt-dissociated total histone and pairs of the histones H2A and H2B as suggested by Kornberg (1974), although it should be noted from recent studies of the cross-linking of histones in chromatin that, except for H1, "the majority of a priori possible histone pairs can be formed" with the cross-linking reagents (Georgiev, 1974). It would appear therefore, that all four histones are in close association in the subunit in chromatin. Van Holde (1974) has suggested a similar "core"-type model, and Kornberg (1974) has made similar suggestions.

The DNA component of chromatin contributes scatter to the rings at 5.5 and 2.7 nm, and a possible interpretation of these data is that each globular unit contains about two turns of a coil of pitch 55 Å wound on the outside of the histone core. A schematic representation of the model of the globular structure is shown in Fig. 1. The basic DNA subunit length of 205 base pairs could be accommodated in such a structure if the mean diameter of the DNA coil is about 10.6 nm. However, since part of this DNA would form links between the globular subunit then depending on the length of the link the mean diameter of the DNA coil

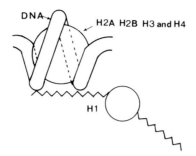

Fig. 1. Schematic representation of a possible model for the chromatin subunit structure. From Baldwin *et al.* (1975) by permission of *Nature* (*London*).

would be reduced. It is possible that the 170-base pair DNA unit observed by Noll (1974) is contained in the globular structure while the additional 35-base pair segment is involved in the linkage, which could also be coiled or folded. A string of such globular units is thought to make up the basic structure of chromatin. Histone H1 is located on the outside of the subunit structure, and there is wide acceptance of the proposal that one of the functions of this histone is to cross-link (Bradbury *et al.*, 1973) and generate the higher-order structures of the eukaryotic chromosome. It is not clear at this stage whether H1 cross-links between globular units within the same string or between different strings.

VI. Histone H1 Phosphorylation and the Cell Cycle

An attractive general hypothesis concerning mechanisms for controlling the structure of the chromosome through the cell cycle is that enzyme-induced chemical modifications of histones are involved in these mechanisms. With only five major histones, a chemical modification of any histone will modify the interactions of that histone with DNA throughout the genome. Further, all chemical modifications so far reported affect the charged state of basic residues or of serines and threonines, and these modified residues are located in or close to the basic segments of the histone molecules. It may be significant that in the model proposed above the basic segments of the histones are complexed with DNA on the outside of the globular subunit and are thus accessible to enzyme modifications. Similarly H1 is also located on the outside of the globular structure and would also be accessible to enzyme action.

Unlike the other histones, H1 exhibits a marked sequence heterogeneity which is both tissue and species specific (Bustin and Cole, 1968, 1969); Rall and Cole, 1970, 1971); Kincade (1969). These histones can be enzymatically phosphorylated at serines (Langan, 1971) and threonines (Langan and Hohman, 1974). Langan has characterized three separate histone phosphokinases HK1, HK2, and HKG; HK1 is cyclic AMP (cAMP)-dependent and phosphorylates H1 specifically at serine 37; HK2 is independent of cAMP and phosphorylates calf H1 *in vitro* specifically at serine 106, while HKG is a growth-associated cAMP-independent enzyme which phosphorylates multiple sites of both serine and threonine in both the N and C terminal regions, but not in the apolar central segment (Langan and Hohman, 1974). We have used the true slime mold *Physarum polycephalum* as a model for cell cycle studies in eukaryotes. It contains five major histone fractions and approximately equal amounts of histone and DNA. In the mitotic cycle of *P. polycephalum* G_1 phase, if it exists, is very short since DNA synthesis (S phase) follows mitosis almost immediately, taking 3–4 hours whereas G_2 phase takes about 5 hours. The major advantage of using this organism is that in the plasmodial stage the nuclei go through mitosis synchronously and the highly synchronized divisions (synchronous metaphases of 10^8 nuclei occur within 5 minutes in a division time of 9 hours) have been demonstrated for 5 complete consecutive cycles (Mohberg, 1974). It is possible therefore, with this system, to use long-term labeling for pinpointing both synthesis and chemical modification of nuclear proteins with some accuracy in the cell cycle of *P. polycephalum*.

Phosphorylation of histone H1 has been the subject of detailed studies in many biological systems, and three facts have been established.

1. Chalkley and his co-workers have shown that there is a positive correlation between the phosphate content of H1 and the rate of cell replication in calf (Panyim and Chalkley, 1969), cultured hepatoma cells (Oliver *et al.*, 1972; Balhorn *et al.*, 1972a), normal and regenerating rat liver (Balhorn *et al.*, 1971), and rat and mouse tumors (Balhorn *et al.*, 1972b), strongly suggesting that the correlation is general in eukaryotes.

2. Phosphorylation of histone H1 has been observed during S phase in cultured mammalian cells synchronized at mitosis by means of blocking agents and mitotic selection (Balhorn *et al.*, 1972c), which gives synchrony through G_1 and S phase but not through G_2 phase (Gurley *et al.*, 1973). In regenerating rat liver, H1 phosphorylation occurs in the few hours before mitosis (Stevely and Stocken, 1968; Balhorn *et al.*, 1971, 1972b), but it is not possible in this system to distinguish between S phase and G_2 phase, and this high phosphate content could not be correlated with DNA synthesis or with the initiation of mitosis. It should be emphasized that in the above experiments only the simple incorporation of phosphate into the histones was measured, and it was not known whether this phosphorylation was a net increase in the number of phosphate groups per H1 molecule or the phosphorylation of newly synthesized H1 during S phase. Because of the precise synchrony of nuclear divisions in

the plasmodial stage of *P. polycephalum* over several cycles, long-term double-labeling experiments could be performed (Bradbury *et al.*, 1973c) to determine the net change in phosphate content of the *P. polycephalum* histone H1 through the cell cycle. Histones were labeled with lysine-^{3}H and ^{32}P, and the ratio ^{32}P/^{3}H lysine was measured through the cell cycle. It was found that this ratio was constant through S phase but showed a large peak in late G_2 phase. Since histones are synthesized during S phase, the constant ratio of ^{32}P/^{3}H lysine strongly implies that the phosphorylation observed in S phase is of newly synthesized H1 molecules. These results throw considerable doubt on the significance of the S phase phosphorylation, although the possibility that different sites of phosphorylation are involved cannot be excluded. This doubt has been strengthened recently by studies of the coupling of S phase phosphorylation and DNA synthesis (Balhorn *et al.*, 1973) and by the work of Marks *et al.* (1973) with synchronized HeLa S-3 cells.

3. Most of the phosphorylation of *P. polycephalum* H1 occurs in late G2 phase, and at this time there is a large increase in the net phosphate content per H1 molecule. Increased H1 phosphorylation has also been observed in mammalian cells in late G_2 (Gurley *et al.*, 1973), mostly in the 3 hours before metaphase (Gurley *et al.*, 1974) in agreement with the *P. polycephalum* results. Further, the phosphate content of H1 is enhanced in metaphase cells (Lake and Salzman, 1972) and dephosphorylation occurs when the cell move into G_1 (Lake, 1973). These data are consistent with the very precise timing in *P. polycephalum* which located the peaks of maximum *P. polycephalum* H1 phosphate content at the time of chromosome condensation (Bradbury *et al.*, 1973c). Thus phosphorylation of H1 has been proposed as the initiation step in mitosis. The basic idea behind this proposal is that phosphorylation of the H1 molecule modifies their interactions in chromatin, resulting in the initial stages of chromosome condensation. Although we are more concerned with growth-associated phosphorylation in these processes, it has been shown by nuclear magnetic resonances studies that there is a marked difference in the interaction with DNA of histone H1 phosphorylated at serines 37 and 106 when compared to the behavior of the control nonphosphorylated H1. At 0.35 M NaCl the control H1 is fully bound to the DNA whereas a large portion of the phosphorylated H1, probably the amino half of the molecule, is free from the DNA (E. M. Bradbury, S. E. Danby, T. A. Langan, and H. W. E. Rattle, unpublished).

Clearly it is important to know whether the H1 phosphorylation is a consequence of an increase in availability of the substrate, possibly through a change in chromosome structure, or whether it results from a change in enzyme activity. The latter would strongly imply that *P.*

polycephalum H1 phosphorylation is an essential preliminary step in chromosome condensation. H1 phosphorylating activity [i.e., the net activity of histone phosphokinase and histone phosphatase (Langan, 1971)] has been monitored through the mitotic cycle of *P. polycephalum* by measuring the phosphorylating activity of nuclei, isolated at different stages of the cycle, acting on excess added calf thymus H1 histone as substrate (Bradbury *et al.*, 1974a). It was found that the enzyme activity increased exponentially by 16-fold from a minimum near metaphase to a maximum in late G_2 (1.75 hours before metaphase) and then fell rapidly to a minimum before the start of the next cycle. The peak in activity preceded the maximum in *P. polycephalum* H1 phosphate content as might be expected if the activity is controlling the phosphate content. Further, a detailed comparison of the variation in enzyme activity with results obtained from plasmodial fusion (Carlile and Dee, 1967; Chin *et al.*, 1972), addition of plasmodial extracts (Oppenheim and Katzir, 1971), and heat shock (Brewer and Rusch, 1968) showed that it agreed closely with the behavior expected of a "mitotic trigger." It has been proposed, therefore, that the cyclic variation in phosphorylating activity is involved in the control of cell division and that the phosphorylation of the very lysine-rich histone H1 is the initiation step in chromosome condensation. Since H1 is largely dephosphorylated before completion of metaphase, it is thought that a second process or more processes, complete the final steps of condensation to metaphase chromosome.

In a direct test of these proposals, heterologous growth-associated histones phosphokinase HKG from Ehrlich ascites was added to the growing plasmodia of *P. polycephalum*. It was found that if the enzyme was added during the normal rise in endogenous phosphorylating activity it resulted in a highly significant acceleration of the initiation of mitosis (Bradbury *et al.*, 1974b). In control experiments the inactivated enzyme and other proteins were found to have no effect. These experiments are subject to some reservation since the heterologous enzyme was a crude preparation and there is no direct evidence that it penetrated into the nucleus.

A summary of the phosphorylation studies of H1 in *Physarum polycephalum* is shown in Fig 2. This shows (1) the variation in phosphate uptake of histone H1 through the cell cycle which reaches a maximum about 20 minutes before metaphase, when the chromosomes are observed to be condensing; (2) the variation in phosphorylating activity of the nuclei of *P. polycephalum* which precedes the peak of phosphate content, and (3) the effect on mitosis of adding the heterologous growth-associated histone phosphokinase HKG from Ehrlich ascites.

In general it is thought that whereas doubts can be expressed concern-

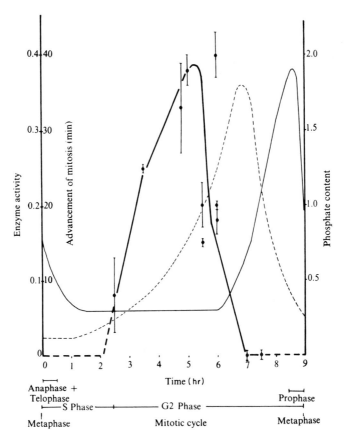

FIG. 2. Curves summarizing the data obtained from studies of the phosphoryl-ation of H1 in the mitotic cycle of *Physarum polycephalum*; (i) the variation in phosphate content of H1 (——); (ii) the variation in endogenous nuclear phos-phorylating activity (- - -); and (iii) advancement of mitosis on addition of heter-ologous Ehrlich ascites H1 phosphokinase at different times in the mitotic cycle (——). From Bradbury *et al.* (1974b) by permission of *Nature (London)*.

ing the last experiment, if taken in isolation, the sum total of these studies strongly supports the proposals concerning the role of histone H1 phos-phorylation in the initiation of chromosome condensation and control of cell division.

VII. Summary

In the past year new proposals have been made concerning the role of histones in chromatin structure and control of cell division. Much evi-dence now supports a globular subunit structure for chromatin. A model is proposed for this structure in which DNA, complexed with the basic segments of histones H2A, H2B, H3 and H4, is coiled on the outside of a core formed by interacting apolar segments. The very lysine-rich histone H1 is located on the outside of this structure. It is significant that the location of the DNA model makes it available both for recognition and enzyme attack and that residues in the basic segments of histones are also available for chemical modification. It is well known that chemical modifications of histones occur at residues in the basic segments and an attractive general hypothesis is that these modifications control the interactions between histones and DNA throughout the genome. In this respect, phosphorylation of H1 is of considerable interest and in the synchronous mitotic cycle of *Physarum polycephalum* it has been found that there is a large net increase in phosphate content of H1 in late G2 just prior to chromosome condensation. Further, this H1 phosphorylation is controlled by a large and cyclical variation in the net phosphorylating activity of the cell nucleus. It has been proposed that the phosphorylation of H1 is involved in the *initial* steps of chromosome condensation and that the cyclical variation in enzyme activity is an important factor in the control of cell division.

ACKNOWLEDGMENTS

The work described in this article has been carried out by my colleagues and co-workers named in the references from this Laboratory. We acknowledge the support of the Science Research Council of the United Kingdom.

REFERENCES

Baldwin, J. P., Boseley, P. G., Bradbury, E. M., and Ibel, K. (1975). *Nature (London)* **253,** 245.

Balhorn, R., Riecke, O., and Chalkley, R. (1971). *Biochemistry* **10,** 3952.

Balhorn, R., Chalkley, R., and Granner, D. (1972a). *Biochemistry* **11,** 1094.

Balhorn, R., M., Balhorn, M., Morris, H. P., and Chalkley, R. (1972b). *Cancer Res.* **32,** 1775.

Balhorn, R., Bordwell, J., Sellers, L., Granner, D., and Chalkley, R. (1972c). *Biochem. Biophys. Res. Commun.* **46,** 1326.

Balhorn, R., Tanphaichitr, N., Chalkley, R., and Granner, D. K. (1973). *Biochemistry* **12,** 5146.

Bradbury, E. M., Molgaard, H. V., Stephens, R. M., Bolund, L. A., and Johns, E. W. (1972). *Eur. J. Biochem.* **31,** 474.

Bradbury, E. M., Cary, P. D., Crane-Robinson, C., and Rattle, H. W. E. (1973a). *Ann. N.Y. Acad. Sci.* **222,** 266.

Bradbury, E. M., Carpenter, B. G., and Rattle, H. W. E. (1973b). *Nature* **241,** 123.

Bradbury, E. M., Inglis, R. J., Matthews, H. R., and Sarner, N. (1973c). *Eur. J. Biochem.* **33,** 131.

Bradbury, E. M., Inglis, R. J., and Matthews, H. R. (1974a). *Nature (London)* **247,** 257.

Bradbury, E. M., Inglis, R. J., Matthews, H. R., and Langan, T. A. (1974b). *Nature (London)* **249,** 553.

Bram, S., and Ris, H. (1971). *J. Mol. Biol.* **55**, 325.

Bram, S., Butler-Browne, G., Bradbury, E. M., Baldwin, J. P., Reiss, C., and Ibel, K. (1974). *Biochimie* **56**, 987.

Brewer, E. N., and Rusch, H. P. (1968). *Exp. Cell Res.* **49**, 79.

Bustin, M., and Cole, R. D. (1968). *J. Biol. Chem.* **243**, 4500.

Bustin, M., and Cole, R. D. (1969). *J. Biol. Chem.* **244**, 5286.

Carlile, M., and Dee, J. (1967). *Nature (London)* **215**, 832.

Chin, B., Friedrich, P. D., and Bernstein, I. A. (1972). *J. Gen. Microbiol.* **71**, 93.

Croft, L. R. (1973). "Handbook of Protein Sequences." Joynson-Bruvvers Ltd., Oxford.

D'Anna, J., and Isenberg, I. (1973). *Biochemistry* **12**, 1035.

De Lange, R. G. (1974). CIBA *Struct. Func. Chromatin, Ciba Found. Symp.* No. 28, p. 59.

De Lange, R. G., Fambrough, D. M., Smith, E. L., and Bonner, J. (1969a). *J. Biol. Chem.* **244**, 319.

De Lange, R. G., Fambrough, D. M., Smith, E. L., and Bonner, J. (1969b). *J. Biol. Chem.* **244**, 5669.

Georgiev, G. P. (1975). *In* "The Structure and Function of Chromatin," *Ciba Found. Symp.* **28**, p. 48. Elsevier, Amsterdam.

Gurley, L. R., Walters, R. A., and Tobey, R. A., (1973). *Biochem. Biophys. Res. Commun.* **50**, 744.

Gurley, L. R., Walters, R. A., and Tobey, R. A. (1974). *J. Cell. Biol.* **60**, 356.

Hewish, D. R., and Burgoyne, L. A. (1973). *Biochem. Biophys. Res. Commun.* **52**, 504.

Isenberg, I. (1974). "Nuclear Proteins, Chromatin Structure, and Gene Regulation," Gordon Conf.

Jones, G. M. T., Rall, S. C., and Cole, R. D. (1974). *J. Biol. Chem.* **249**, 2548.

Kincade, J. M., (1969). *J. Biol. Chem.* **244**, 3375.

Kornberg, R. D. (1974). *Science* **184**, 868.

Kornberg, R. D., and Thomas, I. D. (1974). *Science* **184**, 865.

Lake, R. S. (1973). *Nature (London), New Biol.* **242**, 145.

Lake, R. S., and Salzman, N. P. (1972). *Biochemistry* **11**, 4817.

Langan, T. A. (1971). *Ann. N.Y. Acad. Sci.* **185**, 166.

Langan, T. A., and Hohman, P. (1974). *Fed. Proc. Fed. Amer. Soc. Exp. Biol.* **33**, 1597. (Abstr. No. 2111).

Lewis, P. N., and Bradbury, E. M. (1974). *Biochim. Biophys. Acta* **336**, 153.

Lewis, P. N., Bradbury, E. M., and Crane-Robinson, C. (1974). *Biochemistry* (in press).

Marks, D. B., Paik, W. K., and Borun, T. W. (1973). *J. Biol. Chem.* **248**, 5600.

Mohberg, I. (1974). *In* "The Cell Nucleus" (H. Busch, ed.), Vol. 1, p. 187. Academic Press, New York.

Moore, P. B., Engleman, D. M., and Schoenburn, B. P. (1974). *Proc. Nat. Acad. Sci. U.S.* **71**, 172.

Neelin, J. M. (1964). *In* "The Nucleohistones" (J. Bonner and P.O.P. T'so eds.), p. 66. Holden-Day, San Francisco, California.

Noll, M. (1974). *Nature (London)* **251**, 249.

Olins, A. D., and Olins, D. E. (1973). *J. Cell Biol.* **59**, 2520.

Olins, A. D., and Olins, D. E. (1974). *Science* **183**, 330.

Oliver, D., Balhorn, R., Granner, D., and Chalkey, R. (1972). *Biochemistry* **11**, 3921.

Oppenheim, A., and Katzir, N. (1971). *Exp. Cell Res.* **68**, 224.

Panyim, S., and Chalkley, R. (1969). *Biochemistry* **8**, 3972.

Pardon, J. F., and Wilkins, M. H. F. (1972). *J. Mol. Biol.* **68**, 115.

Rall, S. C., and Cole, R. D. (1970). *J. Biol. Chem.* **245**, 1458.

Rall, S. C., and Cole, R. D. (1971). *J. Biol. Chem.* **246**, 7175.

Rill, R., and van Holde, K. E. (1973). *J. Biol. Chem.* **248**, 1080.

Sahasrabuddhe, C. G., and van Holde, K. E. (1974). *J. Biol. Chem.* **249**, 152.

Stevely, W. S., and Stocken, L. A. (1968). *Biochem. J.* **110**, 187.

Stuhrmann, H. B. (1974). *J. Appl. Crystallogr.* **7**, 173.

van der Westhuyzen, D. R., and von Holt, C. (1971). *FEBS (Fed. Eur. Biochem. Soc.) Lett.* **14**, 333.

Van Holde, K. E. (1974). Symposium "Organization and Transcription of the Nuclear Genome in Eukaryotes." Strasbourg, April (1974).

Wilkins, M. H. F. (1964). "The Cell Nucleus," Gordon Research Conference, New Hampshire, U.S.

Woodcock, C. L. F. (1973). *J. Cell Biol.* **59**, 368a.

CHAPTER 2

CONTROL OF GENE EXPRESSION DURING THE TERMINAL DIFFERENTIATION OF ERYTHROID CELLS

A. Fantoni, M. Lunadei,* and E. Ullu†

LABORATORIO DI RADIOBIOLOGIA ANIMALE
C.S.N. CASACCIA, CNEN
ROME, ITALY

I. Introduction

The study of sequential differentiative events allows one to distinguish three main stages in the differentiation of mammalian erythroid cells. A first stage is characterized by the transition from "stem" cells, which are common precursors to different cell populations, to cells "committed" to differentiate to a single type of cell. Indeed, if one accepts the hypothesis of differential gene expression as the molecular basis of differentiation, the commitment of a cell to differentiate into an x cell instead of a y cell must depend on whether the X set of genes has the possibility of being expressed in this cell line, while the expression of the Y set of genes becomes permanently repressed.

During the second stage committed cells are induced to express the genes for the specialized proteins (i.e., globin chains in erythroid cells), thus becoming "irreversibly committed" cells; the phenotypic expression of genes typical of the differentiated cell population may be under hormonal control (i.e., prolactin inducing the synthesis of milk proteins).

* II Cattedra di Biologia Generale, Università di Roma, Policlinico Umberto I, Roma, Italy. Supported by Grant C.T.B./72/00826/04 of CNR.

† II Cattedra di Biologia Generale, Università di Roma, Policlinico Umberto I, Roma, Italy. Recipient of a CNR postdoctoral fellowship, N. 201/4/7.

During the third and final stage, which is referred to as terminal differentiation, cells that are already differentiated mature and specialize their function, in that they maintain the capacity to synthesize only the specialized proteins and abolish other important cellular activities, among them cell division. Therefore one may envisage differentiation as the transition of a clone of cells through various morphological and functional stages during which different groups of genes are temporarily expressed, although the greater part of the genome is permanently repressed. Once the cell clone has achieved terminal differentiation, only one set of genes is phenotypically expressed.

According to recent advances in eukaryote biology, it is now possible to describe some factors determining each of these differentiative stages for many cell lines. During erythroid cell development one may easily distinguish stages corresponding to those mentioned above. Hemopoietic stem cells, although not described as yet as a precise morphological entity, may be assayed from their capacity to colonize the spleen of an X-irradiated syngeneic host (Till et al., 1964). Committed erythroid cells are represented by proerythroblasts, which are characterized by their capacity to respond to erythropoietin stimulation with an increase of cell proliferation (Paul and Hunter, 1968) and with the synthesis of globin messengers (Chui et al., 1971; Terada et al., 1972). The differentiated population is formed by all cytological classes of erythroblasts capable of hemoglobin synthesis; the product of terminal erythroid differentiation is the reticulocyte, which is incapable of expressing other genes but for globin chains and which has lost the capacity both for gene replication and for transcription. In Volume 1 of this series, Marks and Kovach (1966) have reviewed the typical features of mammalian erythroid cell development.

Within the general pattern of differentiative processes, terminal differentiation is endowed with the following peculiar features: (1) After the capacity to synthesize the specialized proteins is established, a precise number of cell divisions is performed. This process brings the population of differentiated cells to a constant, physiological size, after which no further increase is observed. (2) The transcription of most genes necessary both for cell "household" and for the specialized proteins is discontinued. (3) Messenger RNAs (mRNAs) for the specialized proteins are "stabilized," as they maintain the capacity to direct protein synthesis under conditions where gene transcription is blocked. (4) Also the final concentration of specialized proteins present in each mature, differentiated cell is constant; after this concentration has been reached, the synthesis of specialized proteins is discontinued.

Thus, it would seem that terminal differentiation is not produced by a simple process of "exhaustion" of most cell functions. Indeed, the fact that each event seems to be programmed for precise quantitative features suggests that "exhaustion" cannot be random, but must be controlled.

II. Terminal Differentiation of Erythroid Cells

In this paper data are presented relative to the differentiation of erythroid cells derived from the yolks sac (YSEC) of fetal mice. This erythroid population may be considered as a experimental model particularly fit for studies on terminal differentiation. The development of erythroid cells derived from the yolk sac of fetal mice has been described for the morphological and biochemical patterns in previous papers (Marks and Kovach, 1966; Marks et al., 1968; Fantoni et al., 1969b). For the sake of clarity some general characteristics of the yolk sac erythroid population are described.

The first erythropoietic site of mouse embryos becomes apparent by day 8 of fetal development in the yolk sac blood islands (Attfield, 1951; Borghese, 1959). As shown in Fig. 1, early precursors of erythroid cells (mostly basophilic erythroblasts) proliferate in the yolk sac during days 9 and 10 of fetal development. During day 9 blood vessels connect the yolk sac to the embryo and erythroid cells are transferred to the fetal

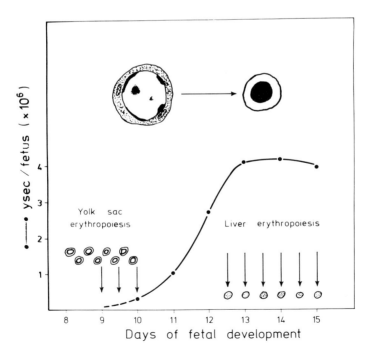

FIG. 1. Terminal differentiation of yolk sac-derived erythroid cells (YSEC) in mouse fetuses.

circulation; at the end of day 10 extravascular areas of the yolk sac appear completely depleted of erythroblasts. From day 10 to day 15 of gestation, yolk sac-derived erythroid cells (YCEC) proliferate and continue to differentiate in the fetal circulation. Except where it is otherwise stated, the YSEC population studied is from fetuses of the C57Bl strain.

The most important morphological characteristics observed during YSEC differentiation are the following (Kovach *et al.*, 1967; Bank *et al.*, 1970): (1) persistence of nuclei until terminal stages of maturation, similarly to adult avian erythropoiesis; (2) progressive condensation of nuclear chromatin, starting with areas next to the membrane, until by day 14 heterochromatization is complete; (3) decrease of the cortical zone of nucleoli, which disappear completely also by day 14; (4) polyribosomes and mitochondria, which by days 9 and 10 are present in large amounts, disappear progressively from the cytoplasm of YSEC from day 11 to day 14.

Some cytological aspects of YSEC development in mouse fetuses render this population particularly fit for biochemical studies of terminal differentiation. Indeed, during every stage of differentiation the population appears to be highly homogeneous, as if it were produced by a single differentiative event of a limited number of stem cells giving rise to clones whose development is simultaneous. Furthermore, starting from day 10 the population may be entirely removed from the fetal circulation and utilized as such for biochemical analysis. In fact no other cytological species of blood cells contaminates YSEC until late day 12, when liver erythropoiesis begins to deliver reticulocytes to the circulation; besides, the reticulocyte population present in growing proportions after day 12 (Craig and Russell, 1964), being anucleated, cannot interfere with experiments in which DNA and RNA synthesis are studied in YSEC; eventually, also hemoglobin (Hb) synthesis can be studied after day 12 without risk of contamination, as in YSEC the specialized gene products are formed (Fantoni *et al.*, 1967) of Hb E_I, E_{II}, E_{III} (composed of globin chains α, x, y, and z) while liver derived reticulocytes synthesize only Hb A (whose globin chains are α and β). In any case, a method of density fractionation on silicon oils is available (Kovach *et al.*, 1967; Fantoni *et al.*, 1968) which allows a 95% purification of both the YSEC population and the liver-derived reticulocytes.

In the following sections are described the basic biochemical aspects of YSEC terminal differentiation.

A. DNA REPLICATION

From day 10 of fetal development, when the YSEC population is completely released from the yolk sac, to the final erythroid maturation at day 14, the YSEC population performs at least 4 cycles of cell divisions (Fantoni *et al.*, 1972a); this is apparent from the number of YSEC present per fetus, shown in Fig. 1. The doubling time is 12 hours from day 10 to day 11, 18 hours from day 11 to day 12, and longer than 24 hours from day 12 to day 13; only a few cells divide after day 13. These data correlate well with the mitotic index which decreases from 3.5% at day 10–11 to 0.4% at day 13 (de la Chapelle *et al.*, 1969).

Results of experiments measuring DNA synthesis indicate that the population is actively engaged in DNA replication until day 12, while decreasing such activity thereafter, with a complete block occurring at day 14 (de la Chapelle *et al.*, 1969). Contrary to the case in other differentiating cell lines, in this population the simultaneous occurrence of replication and the expression of specialized genes is observed: the implications of this observation, reported by de la Chapelle *et al.* (1969), are discussed in detail by Marks and Rifkind (1972). It may be also relevant to add that none of the processes of cell division occurring from day 10 to day 14 is stimulated by erythropoietin (Paul and Hunter, 1969), thus demonstrating that within this period of development the YSEC population is indeed undergoing terminal differentiation.

B. GENE TRANSCRIPTION

A progressive decrease of ribosome content is observed from day 10 to day 14. At day 14 ribosome content averages one-sixth of the content at day 11 (Fantoni *et al.*, 1968). During the same period the rate of ribosomal gene transcription is decreased about 20-fold, as measured from the rate of formation of nucleolar 45 S preribosomal RNA (Fantoni *et al.*, 1972b). On the other hand, the processing of 45 S RNA to cytoplasmic 18 S + 28 S RNA is much less efficient in younger erythroblasts at day 10 than in more mature erythroblasts at day 14 (see Table I). Therefore it would seem that during terminal differentiation a mechanism is operating which, by increasing the quantitative efficiency of ribosomal RNA processing, results in a greater capacity to build up ribosomes, thus overcoming the relative transcriptional inefficiency. In other words, a post-transcriptional control of ribosome synthesis is performed; this is inversely correlated to the rate of ribosomal gene transcription (Fantoni and Bordin, 1971).

Within the overall decrease of RNA synthetic capacity, the rate of transcription of ribosomal genes is decreased to a greater extent than the synthetic rate of giant-sized, heterogeneous nuclear RNA (Terada *et al.*, 1971). Data reported also by Terada and co-workers (1971) suggest that the mRNAs for globin chains are formed prior to day 10 of fetal development. Newly made, nonribosomal RNA found associated

TABLE I

Processing of Ribosomal RNA in Differentiating
Yolk Sac Erythroid Cells[a]

Time point (minutes)	Nucleolar RNA		Cytoplasmic RNA	
	45 S	32 S	28 S	18 S
Day 10				
15	100			
55	49	45	5	6
90	30	63	12	6
Day 13				
15	100			
55	25	70	29	31
90	17	28	76	43

[a] RNA of yolk sac erythroid cells at days 10 and 13 was pulse labeled for 10 minutes with methylmethionine-^{3}H; radioactivity was then chased by a large excess of methylmethionine for 55 and 90 minutes. RNA was quantitatively recovered from nucleolar and cytoplasmic fractions and each molecular species of ribosomal RNA was isolated by acrylamide gel electrophoresis. The numbers represent the amount of radioactivity as tritiated methyl groups found in each species of nucleolar and cytoplasmic RNA, calculated for each time point and related to the radioactivity present in nucleolar 45 S RNA after a 10-minute pulse, which is made equal to 100. This table is adapted from Fantoni et al. (1972b).

with polyribosomes from day 11 to day 13 appears to be a species of mRNA responsible for histone synthesis; the formation of these mRNAs ceases at day 13, concurrently with the block of nonheme protein synthesis and with the arrest of YSEC division.

C. Messenger RNA Translation

The formation of nonheme proteins, many of which are nuclear basic proteins, drops to zero from day 10 to day 13 (Fantoni et al., 1968). The synthesis of these proteins is directed by mRNAs, which continue to be produced until day 13, but display a high rate of turnover (Terada et al., 1971); in fact, the capacity to form nonheme proteins is actinomycin sensitive and is directed by messengers that are not "stable" (Fantoni et al., 1968) in that the block of gene transcription is followed within a limited period of time by the arrest of translation.

The overall synthesis of globin chains α, x, y, and z, composing embryonic hemoglobins E_I, E_{II}, E_{III} (Fantoni et al., 1967), does not decrease until day 12 and is lowered thereafter to zero at day 15; starting with day 10 the synthesis of hemoglobin is actinomycin insensitive, and it is therefore directed by a "stable" mRNA (Fantoni *et al.*, 1968). These data correlate with the observations of Terada *et al.* (1971) indicating that messengers for hemoglobins are not produced after day 10.

During the terminal differentiation of YSEC, the relative rates of synthesis of the three embryonic hemoglobins change. The embryonic hemoglobin that is most abundant at day 10, Hb E_I, is a relatively minor component at day 14, at which time Hb E_{II} is the major Hb component (Fantoni *et al.*, 1969a). This change in relative rates of Hb synthesis is observed at a stage of YSEC maturation when hemoglobin mRNA translation does not depend immediately on gene transcription, thus suggesting that it may be due to a regulation operated at the post-transcriptional level.

D. Timing of Major Events during Terminal Differentiation of Yolk Sac Erythroid Cells in Mouse Fetuses

At day 10 the YSEC population has been completely released from the yolk sac site of erythropoiesis to the fetal circulation, where it proliferates actively, but with the kinetic features of a "closed" population. Messenger RNAs for globin chains have been already produced and hemoglobin synthesis has become actinomycin resistant. Hemoglobin formation represents only one-fifth of the total protein-synthesizing capacity.

At day 13 the YSEC population has lost the capacity for DNA replication and for cell division. The formation of polyribosome-associated mRNAs is discontinued; as a consequence the synthesis of nonheme proteins is arrested and the only protein being synthesized is hemoglobin.

At day 15 it has lost also the capacity to form ribosomes and hemoglobin.

III. Hemoglobin Synthesis during Terminal Differentiation is Programmed by Earlier Transcriptional Events

Proteins not directly endowed with the specialized differentiated function, but related to the maintenance of cellular activities, are produced mainly during early stages of maturation; their synthesis shows an immediate temporal dependence on transcriptional events. Singer and Penman (1973) have recently presented evidence for two poly(A) associated mRNA populations in HeLa cells, decaying with a half-life of 24 hours and 7 hours, respectively; in these cells none of the proteins produced performs activities typical of a differentiated state. Similarly, Perry and Kelley (1973) have reported that poly(A) containing mRNAs from *in vitro*-growing nondifferentiated L cells show an average lifetime that is roughly equivalent to one cell generation; non-poly(A)-containing messengers, such as the ones for histones, retain their activity only for a period of time equivalent to S phase in HeLa cells.

Conversely, the synthesis of specialized proteins, such as hemoglobin, does not seem to be dependent on transcriptional events within a short time interval. Indeed, the average lifetime of mRNA for hemoglobin is by no means related to the cell cycle, as it is known to be over 3 days in nondividing reticulocytes and to last for 5 days over at least four cell cycles in differentiating YSEC. In agreement with these data, it is possible that in early stages of differentiation, prior to day 10, there is a transcriptional event programming the total amount of hemoglobin produced by the erythroid cell clone. That is, the number of hemoglobin genes transcripts present in erythroid precursors may be controlling directly the extent of expression of hemoglobin genes during terminal differentiation. Alternatively, it is also possible that during terminal differentiation minor transcriptional events, with regulatory function and not detectable by biochemical analysis, may specifically affect mRNAs for hemoglobin and may thus regulate the amount of hemoglobin accumulated in mature erythroid cells. This possibility is in agreement with the hypothesis of the regulatory function of reiterated transcripts (Britten and Davidson, 1969) and it is consistent with the data presented in previous sections indicating changes in the relative rates of synthesis for the three embryonic hemoglobins during terminal differentiation.

In order to distinguish between these two hypotheses, it might be useful to produce experimentally a population of YSEC with a normal amount of DNA and with a normal synthetic capacity for RNA, but containing a larger amount of cytoplasmic structures responsible for translation. Thus, we attempted to dissociate the amounts of transcriptional units from the amount of translational structures present in the YSEC population. This experimental tool was the result of the observation that in the population of yolk sac erythroid cells irradiated *in vivo* with 120 rads at day 10, cell division is arrested by day 12, thus omitting the last cell cycle.

Indeed, yolk sac erythroid cells subjected to X-ray irradiation at day 10 of fetal development increase their number by cell division until day 12 in a fashion similar to the normal yolk sac erythroid cell population (Fig. 2a). From day 10 to day 12 the increase in cell number in both the normal and irradiated populations accounts for about three cell cycles. After day 12 the number of irradiated cells does not increase any further (Fig. 2a) whereas the number of normal erythroid cells doubles once more between day 12 and 13.

This is interpreted as being due to a block of cell division after day

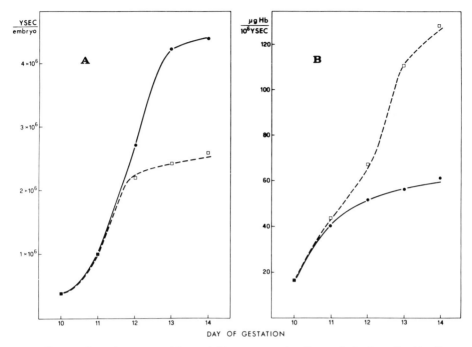

FIG. 2. Growth curve and hemoglobin content of yolk sac-derived erythroid cells (YSEC) from normal (●——●) and from irradiated (□- - -□) mouse fetuses at days 10, 11, 12, 13, and 14 of fetal development. (A) Number of yolk sac erythroid cells (YSEC) per fetus. (B) Content of embryonic hemoglobins per 10^6 yolk sac-derived erythroid cells. Pregnant mice were irradiated at day 10 of gestation with 120 rads. The techniques for cell enumeration, for the isolation of hemoglobin by acrylamide gel electrophoresis, and for the determination of hemoglobin content are described by Fantoni et al. (1972a). Adapted from Fantoni et al. (1972a).

12, that is, after three cell cycles have been completed, as indicated by the fact that the content of hemoglobin shows only a small increase in irradiated cells before day 12 whereas at day 13 irradiated erythroid cells contain at least a double amount of hemoglobin as compared with normal cells (Fig. 2b).

Indeed, undivided YSEC at day 13 are larger cells because their cytoplasm is twice as abundant as in divided YSEC. DNA content in control YSEC shows a pattern (see Table II) indicating a decrease from values at day 10 close to the 4n content typical of mice (Laird, 1954) toward values at day 13 strictly similar to the corresponding diploid content. This pattern is suggestive of a progressive increase of the G_1 period of the cellular cycle and of a lower percentage of cells of the YSEC population which are in the late S and G_2 periods. A different pattern is shown

TABLE II

DNA CONTENT AND RNA SYNTHESIS IN NORMAL AND IN
X-IRRADIATED YOLK SAC ERYTHROID CELLS (YSEC)[a]

YSEC population	Day 10	Day 11	Day 12	Day 13
Normal				
DNA content	11.9	11.2	9.7	7.2
RNA synthesis	3.1	2.7	1.3	0.7
X-Irradiated				
DNA content	11.9	10.8	6.5	6.9
RNA synthesis	3.1	2.4	0.9	0.6

[a] DNA content was measured by the modified diphenylamine method of Burton (1955) and expressed as grams^{-12} per cell. RNA synthesis was measured as outlined in Fantoni et al. (1968) and expressed as picomoles of uridine incorporated in RNA contained in 10^6 YSEC during 5 minutes of incubation at 37°C.

by X-irradiated YSEC which reach the diploid value at day 12, when they stop cell division.

RNA synthesis shows one meaningful difference between the two populations. At day 12 the X-irradiated population which has already stopped cell division, and has therefore reached the diploid DNA content, synthesizes RNA at a rate which may be significantly lower than in control YSEC at the same day. This would indicate that, if one disregards possible differences due to the rate of RNA polymerase activity, the number of units of transcription seem to be related to the amount of DNA present. At day 13 no meaningful difference is observed between the two populations both for DNA content and for overall RNA synthesis.

Cell division involves DNA replication and the distribution of an equal and complete set of genes to daughter cells, while preexisting mRNA molecules are shared by the daughter cells. Cells which do not perform the last cycle of cell division contain the same amounts of DNA, but they should contain a double amount of translational structures relative to divided cells. If hemoglobin synthesis is directly controlled by gene transcription at day 13 undivided cells should form hemoglobin at the same rate as divided cells.

In Table III are reported results of experiments aimed at measuring the synthetic capacity for each one of the three embryonic hemoglobins. The data indicate that when irradiated cells stop dividing after day 12, the synthetic capacity is increased in comparison with controls in a similar fashion for the three embryonic hemoglobins. In absolute amounts the three hemoglobins are synthesized at rates at least 2 times higher in nondivided cells at day 13 than in control cells at the same state of

TABLE III

In Vivo SYNTHESIS OF EMBRYONIC HEMOGLOBINS DURING THE DIFFERENTIATION
OF NORMAL AND IRRADIATED YOLK SAC ERYTHROID CELLS (YSEC)[a,b]

Fetal development (days)	Hemoglobin synthesis			
	E_I	E_{II}	E_{III}	Total
Normal YSEC				
10–11	14.5	13.4	8.3	36.2
11–12	12.9	14.7	7.3	34.9
12–13	6.5	11.8	4.0	22.3
Irradiated YSEC				
10–11	17.1	13.1	9.6	39.8
11–12	18.4	19.3	9.4	47.1
12–13	12.6	26.2	8.0	46.8

[a] Adapted from Fantoni (1971).

[b] Hemoglobin synthesis is expressed as micrograms of embryonic hemoglobins E_I, E_{II}, and E_{III} synthesized during the indicated interval of fetal development by 10^6 erythroid cells and measured as reported by Fantoni *et al.* (1972a). The content of each hemoglobin was determined by quantitative recovery of embryonic hemoglobins separated on acrylamide gel electrophoresis as described in Fantoni *et al.* (1969a).

development. Experiments shown in Table III suggest that in nondivided erythroid cells hemoglobin accumulates at a rate double that in normally divided cells. This is because in normally differentiating cells the rate of hemoglobin formation decreases to half from day 12 to day 13, in coincidence with cell division; conversely, in X-irradiated YSEC cell division is not performed between day 12 and day 13, and the capacity to form hemoglobin is maintained at the level of the previous day.

The data shown in Fig. 2 and in Tables II and III suggest that X-irradiation at day 10 allowed us to produce a population of YSEC in which the capacity for gene transcription is dissociated from the capacity for translation of gene transcripts.

It may also be concluded that during terminal differentiation the amount of hemoglobin production is not directly related to the capacity for gene transcription, but it seems rather to depend on the activity of cytoplasmic structures responsible for the translation of previously transcribed genes.

The higher rate of hemoglobin formation observed in undivided cells could be due to a faster rate of messenger readout or alternatively to a greater amount of translational structures. Results shown in Table IV would exclude the former alternative because undivided YSEC at day 13, forming hemoglobin at a rate double that of controls, translate the

TABLE IV

Patterns of Hemoglobin Synthesis in Normal and in
X-Irradiated Yolk Sac Erythroid Cells (YSEC)[a]

Parameter	Normal division		Arrested division	
	Day 12	Day 13	Day 12	Day 13
Number of YSEC/embryo	2.7×10^6	4.4×10^6	2.2×10^6	2.4×10^6
Hemoglobin synthesis in vivo (pmoles/min/10^6 YSEC)	1.62	0.85	2.16	2.02
Rate of globin chain elongation (seconds/chain)	18	16	22	19
Content of ribosomes (pmoles/10^6 YSEC)	0.61	0.44	0.84	0.47

[a] The data reported in this table were obtained from Fantoni et al. (1972a).

hemoglobin messenger at about the same rate as controls (respectively, 19 and 16 seconds per chain). It is also observed that ribosomes are contained in equal amounts in divided and undivided cells at day 13, thus excluding also the possibility that limiting quantities of ribosomes may control aspecifically the capacity to produce hemoglobin. By exclusion it may be suggested that mRNA molecules retaining their capacity to direct hemoglobin synthesis are present in double amount in undivided YSEC.

The results obtained with the YSEC population would then exclude the possibility that during terminal differentiation gene expression is modulated by changing the rate of messenger readout on polyribosomes. This observation should not be considered valid for all erythroid systems: in adult mice the transition from nucleated erythroid cells to reticulocytes is accompanied by a 4-fold increase of the rate of per cell hemoglobin synthesis because in the course of terminal erythroid differentiation ribosomes acquire the capacity to translate the hemoglobin messenger at a higher rate (Bordin et al., 1972). In addition, Conconi and co-workers (1972) have provided evidence that in the Ferrara variant of beta thalassemia the availability of cytoplasmic protein factors determines the capacity of polyribosomal structures to translate mRNA for hemoglobin.

In the YSEC population, the only event determining hemoglobin gene expression during terminal differentiation seems to be the early transcription of the hemoglobin genes into "stable" mRNAs. The stabilization of messangers may be due to a so-called long-lived mRNA—that is, a molecule of mRNA with a very slow turnover—if any (Singer and Leder, 1966); alternatively it might be due to the fact that a mRNA turning over at a normal rate has been preformed in such large amounts as to be not limiting for protein synthesis until the terminal stages of cell maturation. These molecules are not necessarily associated with the poly-ribosomes, but might exist as free ribonucleoproteins in the cytoplasm (Spirin, 1969; Perry and Kelley, 1968; Spohr et al., 1970), which become progressively available for translation and are progressively used up.

According to this hypothesis, it might be expected that the total amount of hemoglobin produced by the progeny of a differentiating ery-throid cell is not dependent on the final number of cells reached by the clone, but rather on the time elapsed since messengers were first synthe-sized and during which messengers are translated.

As shown in Table V, the total amount of each globin chain produced

TABLE V

TOTAL GLOBIN CHAINS SYNTHESIZED BY THE PROGENY OF 10^6 (YSEC) FROM DAY 10 TO DAY 13 OF FETAL DEVELOPMENT[a]

YSEC population	Final progeny of 10^6 YSEC	Total globin chains synthesized (pmoles/72 hours)			
		x Chains	y Chains	z Chains	α Chains
Normal	17.6×10^6	9,520	22,600	5720	28,300
X-irradiated	8.8×10^6	10,400	24,500	5630	30,800

[a] Adapted from Fantoni et al. (1972b).

in the course of terminal differentiation is the same in spite of the arrest of cell division in the irradiated population.

Previous work by Winslow and Ingram (1966), Brawerman and Bank (1969), Fantoni et al. (1968, 1969a), together with the present results may be interpreted as evidence for a model of erythroid differentiation whereby at the onset of differentiation mRNA molecules for hemoglobin are transcribed in much larger amounts than for other proteins in un-differentiated cells. According to this model the production of most mes-sengers is soon discontinued; subsequently, the synthesis of nonheme pro-teins stops long before hemoglobin production because the messenger for hemoglobin is present for a longer period of time in concentrations which are not limiting for protein synthesis. Accordingly, the "stabilization" of hemoglobin formation may simply represent the moment when mRNA for hemoglobin has accumulated in sufficient amounts. The total amount of hemoglobin synthesized during the whole differentiative process of a single cell progeny could be programmed in terms of the number of mRNA molecules produced during the early stages of differentiation.

IV. Final Stages of Protein Synthesis in Differentiated Erythroid Cells: Presence of Inactive Polyribosomes and mRNA Inactivation

During the terminal stages of erythroid differentiation, a continuous decrease of polyribosome content per cell and the reduced availability of mRNAs active for hemoglobin synthesis are observed. In differentiating YSEC, while ribosome formation is continued until complete erythroid maturation (de la Chapelle *et al.*, 1969; Fantoni and Bordin, 1971), the synthesis of mRNAs for hemoglobin is discontinued already in earlier stages of differentiation (Terada *et al.*, 1971), and messenger molecules are progressively used up in the course of hemoglobin accumulation in maturing erythroid cells (Fantoni *et al.*, 1972a).

From day 10 to day 12 of fetal development hemoglobin synthesis is maintained at a constant per cell rate, possibly because neither ribosomes nor mRNA become limiting for protein synthesis; starting with day 12 the capacity for hemoglobin production per cell decreases because cytoplasmic structures responsible for the hemoglobin synthesis are halved in the course of cell division. We intend here to examine the question of whether the expression of hemoglobin genes is arrested in mature erythroid cells because of the relative insufficiency of ribosomes and of other aspecific components of the translational machinery, or alternatively because mRNAs become unable to further direct hemoglobin formation.

In the preceding section it was demonstrated that an X-irradiated population of YSEC stops cell division at day 12, and thereafter, by day 13, it contains a double amount of cytoplasm as compared with normally dividing cells. Nondivided cells synthesize hemoglobin at a rate double that of control cells, in spite of the fact that divided and nondivided cells contain the same amount of ribosomes (see Table IV). It would seem as though normally maturing YSEC contain an amount of ribosomes at least double that necessary for hemoglobin formation, also because no other proteins are synthesized in these cells at day 13.

The relative abundance of ribosomes in YSEC at day 13 could be due to an increased proportion of inactive 80 S monoribosomes. It has been demonstrated (see Fig. 4) that the sucrose density profile is only slightly changed between day 12 and 13, while no difference is seen between the divided and the nondivided population. Together with data shown in table III, the present results indicate that at day 13 normally divided YSEC produce hemoglobin at a 2-fold faster rate, although they contain the same amount of polyribosomes and translate mRNA at the same rate as do nondivided cells. Thus it would seem that in normally maturing erythroid cells polyribosomal structures are present which maintain the aggregated structure, but are inactive for hemoglobin synthesis.

The possibility that part of polyribosomes in normal YSEC at day 13 do not sustain protein synthesis and do not carry growing peptide chains has been tested by incubating YSEC in the presence of ^{14}C-labeled valine and by measuring the incorporation into chains released to the cytoplasm and into growing peptide chains on polyribosomes. Incorporation into finished globin chains is linear within the period of incubation (20 minutes), while incorporation into growing peptide chains on polyribosomes reaches completion after about 4 minutes, that is the time necessary to saturate polyribosomes with growing chains uniformly labeled in the valine residues. As shown in Fig. 3, the specific activity

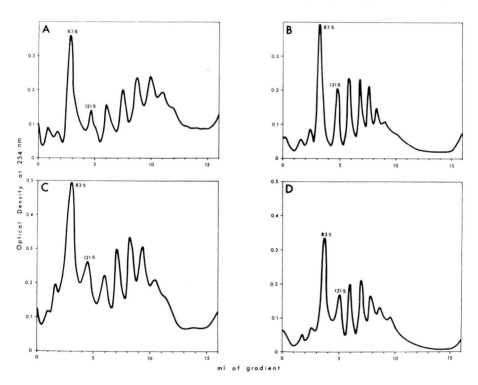

FIG. 3. Gradient sedimentation analysis of ribosomes from yolk sac-derived erythroid cells of normal and irradiated fetuses. (A) Normal fetuses at day 12. (B) Normal fetuses at day 13. (C) Irradiated fetuses at day 12. (D) Irradiated fetuses at day 13. The direction of sedimentation is toward the right of the figure. Adapted from Fantoni et al. (1972a).

(picomoles of valine microgram of ribosomes) is 50% lower in poly-ribosomes from normally maturing cells than in polyribosomes from un-divided cells during both phases of linear increase and saturation.

The results may be utilized to calculate the number of active poly-ribosomes from the number of growing polypeptide chains present per ribosome. Normal YSEC, in which the capacity to produce hemoglobin has been reduced by half in the course of cell division, contain 0.32 pmole of polyribosomes associated with only 0.18 pmole of growing polypeptide chains; in this case about 50% of polyribosomes are not associated with growing peptide chains and may be considered inactive. Conversely, X-irradiated and division-arrested YSEC, in which the capacity to produce hemoglobin has been maintained, contain 0.34 pmole of polyribosomes associated with 0.33 pmole of growing polypeptide chains; in these cells all polyribosomes are active for hemoglobin synthesis.

Taken together, the data shown in Table IV, Fig. 3, and Fig. 4 demon-strate in maturing YSEC the presence of polyribosomes in excess over the capacity to translate mRNA for hemoglobin, but they leave open the possibility that besides polyribosomes, other components necessary for tRNA aminoacylation, chain initiation, elongation, and termination could be deficient for mRNA translation during terminal differentiation. In maturing rabbit reticulocytes a relative decrease of initiation factors (Herzberg et al., 1969) has been demonstrated. In order to exclude this possibility, polyribosomes from normally dividing and from nondivided cells at day 13 have been tested in a cell-free system with an energy regenerating system, crude initiation factors, pH 5 enzyme fraction, and mRNA for hemoglobin—all components being separately tested as active for promoting hemoglobin synthesis by ribosomal subunits (Schreier and Staehelin, 1972). Results shown in Fig. 5 indicate that the specific activity of growing peptide chains (referred to micrograms of polyribosomes) is almost twice lower in polyribosomes from normally dividing YSEC than in nondivided erythroid cells, thus confirming the results obtained with the whole cells and suggesting that in normally maturing YSEC the reason of the reduced capacity for hemoglobin synthesis must be sought in polyribosomal structures.

In other words, polyribosomes are inactive not because they are miss-ing factors necessary for translation, but possibly because the source of mRNA stored in extraribosomal structures (Spirin, 1969; Perry and Kelley, 1968; Spohr et al., 1970) has been depleted and the mRNA mole-cules present on polyribosomes are rendered unsuitable to further direct hemoglobin synthesis. Indeed the pattern of polyribosomes destruction in maturing erythroblasts may offer information of value in answering the question of how messenger molecule is progressively inactivated. Con-flicting evidence in the literature indicates a stepwise disassembly of

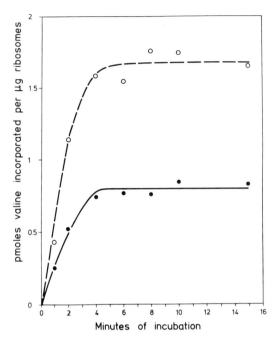

FIG. 4. *In vitro* hemoglobin synthesis by yolk sac-derived erythroid cells from normal (●——●) and irradiated (○- - -○) fetuses at day 13 of fetal development. Valine incorporation is expressed as picomoles per microgram of ribosomes. Erythroid cells (10 to 15 × 10⁶) were resuspended in 100 μl of Krebs-Ringer–bicarbonate medium and preincubated for 3 minutes at 37°C. ¹⁴C-labeled valine was added at time 0. Incubation was blocked by the addition of 50 volumes of ice-cold isotonic medium. The procedures for cell lysis and for determination of the valine pool size are described in Fantoni *et al.* (1968). Techniques for the isolation of ribosomes and for the radio-activity measurements are described in Bordin *et al.* (1972). Both populations of yolk sac erythroid cells were contaminated by reticulocytes derived from the liver, which make only adult hemoglobin (Fantoni *et al.*, 1967). This contamination is very similar in the normal and irradiated populations (respectively, 23% and 25%).

polyribosomes to monoribosomes, which are eventually removed from the cell (Marks *et al.*, 1963; Rowley, 1965; Danon and Cividalli, 1968) or the maintenance of aggregated polyribosomes, which are finally destroyed as such (Glowacki and Millette, 1965; Burka and De Bellis, 1967; De Bellis, 1969; Fantoni *et al.*, 1972a). The former model suggests that the messenger is inactivated in that it is incapable of reinitiating protein synthesis, while the latter model would rather indicate that mRNA is inactivated when the termination of its translation is prevented.

Polyribosomal structures inactive in hemoglobin synthesis may result from a block of termination, which would leave unfinished globin chains bound to polyribosomes; such polyribosomes would not be able to release ribosomal subunits.

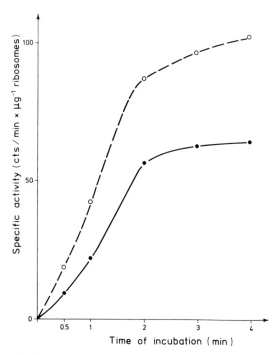

Fɪɢ. 5. Growth of peptide chains on polyribosomes in conditions of cell-free protein synthesis. Polyribosomes from normally dividing erythroid cells at day 13 (●———●); Polyribosomes from X-irradiated, nondividing erythroid cells at day 13 (○- - -○). Ribosomes (15 pmoles) from normally dividing and from nondividing erythroid cells at day 13 have been incubated in 0.1 ml final volume at 35°C for 7 minutes in the presence of 20 mM HEPES pH 7.5, 70 mM KCl, 3.5 mM Mg acetate, 4 mM β-mercaptoethanol, 1 mM ATP, 0.4 mM GTP, 20 mM creatine phosphate, 4 units of creatine phosphate kinase, 30 μM each of the ʟ-amino acids, 0.07 μCi ^{14}C-labeled leucine (final specific activity 15 mCi/mmole), 40 μl of pH 5 enzyme fraction containing 0.7 μg of protein and 31 μg of tRNA, 55 μg of crude initiation factors and 10 pmoles of 9 S mRNA. At the time points indicated, the cell-free mixtures have been examined in a concave exponential sucrose gradient, and the radioactivity recovered in the polyribosomal (120 S) areas has been pooled, determined, and related to the OD$_{260}$ of the same portion of the gradient, as specific activity (counts per minute $\times$ μg^{-1} ribosomes). Ribosome content was determined assuming an extinction coefficient of 13.5 OD$_{260\,nm}$ units per milligram of ribosomes.

Chain termination by polyribosomes from both populations of erythroid cells has been tested by the capacity to release "runoff" 80 S monomers. The presence of runoff monomers in condition of cell-free protein synthesis has been measured from the capacity to translate polyuridylic acid [poly(U)]

In conditions of cell-free protein synthesis, polyribosomes whose ter-

mination is blocked should not release runoff 80 S monomers and therefore should not allow the successive translation of another messenger,
such as poly(U). As shown in Fig. 6, ribosomes from divided cells at
day 13, many of which are inactive, translate poly(U) at a rate half
that of ribosomes from nondivided cells, which are all active in protein
synthesis.

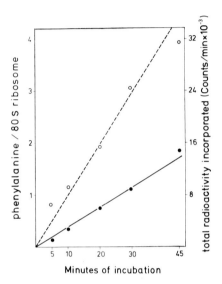

FIG. 6. Translation of the poly(U) messenger by polyribosomes from divided and
nondivided erythroid cells. The assay system contained in a 125-μl volume, 10 pmoles
of ribosomes, 700 μg of pH 5 enzyme fraction, 310 nCi of Amersham ^{14}C-labeled
L-phenylalanine (344 μCi/μmole), 80 mM KCl, 9 mM Mg acetate, 20 mM Tris
pH 7.5, 4 mM β-mercaptoethanol, 1 mM ATP, 0.4 mM GTP, 20 mM creatine phosphate, and 4 units of creatine phosphate kinase. Incubation was at 37°C. At the
different time points indicated, 20-μl aliquots were removed and processed for hot
trichloroacetic acid-precipitable radioactivity. Results are expressed both as total
radioactivity incorporated in the assay system and as moles of phenyl alanine incorporated in 1 mole of 80 S ribosomes. ●——●, Ribosomes from normal, divided
cells; ○- - -○, ribosomes from irradiated, nondivided cells.

One may speculate that this difference may arise from a polymerization produced exclusively by the 80 S (monomer) fraction of ribosomes,
which may originally have been present in different amounts in the two
erythroid populations. This hypothesis, however, is inconsistent with data
showing that at day 13 divided and nondivided cells contain exactly the
same amount of single (80 S) ribosomes (that is respectively, 0.13 pmole
an 0.14 pmole/10^6 cells).

By the criteria of poly(U) translation, inactive polyribosomes seem to be incapable of releasing runoff 80 S monomers as compared with active polyribosomes from undivided cells.

The possibility that in maturing erythroblasts polyribosomes are inactivated following a block of chain termination has also been explored by measuring the capacity to form subunits from runoff 80 S monomers. As indicated in Fig. 7, equal amounts of both ribosome preparations have been incubated in conditions of cell-free system optimal for endogeneous activity, in the presence of saturating amounts of pH 5 enzyme contain-

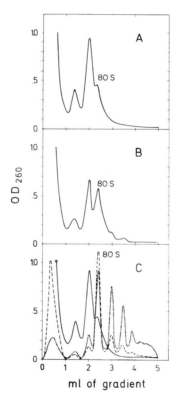

Fig. 7. High-salt sucrose gradient analysis of polyribosomes incubated in conditions of cell-free protein synthesis. (A) Polyribosomes from X-irradiated nondividing erythroid cells at day 13. (B) Polyribosomes from normally dividing erythroid cells at day 13. (C) Polyribosomes from adult mouse liver incubated in normal conditions of cell-free protein synthesis (———); in the absence of the energy regenerating system, but in the presence of pH 5 enzyme fraction (- - - -), in the absence of both the energy-regenerating system and the pH 5 enzyme fraction (. . . .). Twenty picomoles of polyribosomes were incubated for 45 minutes at 35°C essentially as described for Fig. 5, except that crude initiation factors and mRNA for hemoglobin were omitted.

ing polymerizing and terminating factors, but in the absence of exogenous initiation factors and mRNA. These conditions allow for the formation of runoff 80 S monomers only from polyribosomes actively engaged in protein synthesis; the presence of other monomers produced by RNase attack on polyribosomes (Falvey and Staehelin, 1970), and therefore carrying unfinished peptide chains and messenger fragments, can be discriminated against after sucrose gradient centrifugation in the presence of 300 mM KCl and 3 mM Mg acetate. Indeed, these ionic conditions promote the dissociation to subunits only from 80 S monomers produced after a normal pattern of chain termination has occurred (Falvey and Staehelin, 1970; Schreier and Staehelin, 1972).

The results of such an experiment are shown in Fig. 7 and suggest that many more ribosomal subunits are formed by ribosomes from erythroid cells whose division has been arrested than by ribosomes from cells undergoing a normal pattern of cell division. Indeed polyribosomes which are all active in hemoglobin synthesis dissociate almost completely to ribosomal subunits; a small peak of 80 S monomers still present is indicative of some polyribosomal degradation by RNase activity. Polyribosomes from normally maturing cells which are only 50% active dissociate to subunits in smaller amounts, leaving a large peak of 80 S monomers.

The conditions of cell-free systems (see Figs. 6 and 7) are such as to exclude any difference of activity which does not arise from the ribosomes themselves. The source and amount of pH 5 enzyme (containing polymerization and termination factors, together with tRNAs and aminoacyl synthetases) is the same, prepared from ribosome-free mouse liver homogenate, and does not limit the rate of polymerization.

Thus, maturing erythroid cells accumulate polyribosomes that are inactive because incapable of releasing runoff 80 S monomers under conditions of protein synthesis. Our data seem to exclude that this may be due to the absence of protein factors responsbile for the release of complete polypeptide chains. Alternatively, this may be related to a damage of the translated portion of the endogenous messenger molecules; at day 12 functional mRNA molecules are present in amounts limiting for hemoglobin synthesis; they could be maintained in full amounts when cell division is blocked, while their number could be decreased to half in cells undergoing normal division. In order to promove a block of termination the 3'OH terminal should be cleaved; recent evidence in the literature suggests that in eukaryotes extremely long-lived messenger molecules (up to 2 weeks for messengers injected into frog oocytes, see Gurdon *et al.*, 1973) are slowly degraded (Perry and Kelley, 1973; Singer and Penman, 1973), parallel to the removal of the poly(A) segment at the 3'OH terminal (Perry and Kelley, 1973; Scheiness and Darnell, 1973).

The present evidence supports an interpretation of the final stages of mRNA translation whereby the polyribosomes maintain their aggregate structure when the molecule of mRNA they are translating becomes unsuitable for further direct protein synthesis. This may happen, for instance, if the 3'OH terminal of mRNA is cleaved and mRNA loses the proper signals to terminate polypeptide chains; this arrest of termination could promote a structural block of the ribosomal function, thus arresting also the initiation and elongation of polypeptide chains.

V. Concluding Comment

Terminal differentiation has been studied in the yolk sac-derived erythroid population of fetal mice, in an attempt to describe the events that control the total amount of hemoglobin accumulated per cell in the mature erythroid population and that are responsible for the erythroid function.

The regulatory change programming the extent of hemoglobin gene expression is a transcriptional event produced in the early stages of differentiation, most probably during the 48-hour interval between the beginning of hemoglobin synthesis at day 8 and the stage of late basophilic erythroblasts at day 10 of fetal development. After this early transcriptional event no subsequent factor seems to be present that may modulate the rate of hemoglobin formation either by inducing new synthesis of mRNA or by modifying the capacity for globin messengers translation. Indeed, the amount of hemoglobin formed by the erythroid cell clone is programmed in terms of the number of mRNA molecules which have been synthesized before day 10 and is subsequently halved by cell division, until it becomes insufficient to direct hemoglobin synthesis.

The arrest of hemoglobin production is accompanied by the formation of polyribosomes which maintain the aggregated structure but are inactive in protein synthesis; inactive polyribosomes may not be reactivated *in vitro* by the addition of any of the factors necessary for protein synthesis; polyribosome inactivation seems rather to be due to damage at the 3'OH terminal of the translated mRNA sequence, thus confirming that the availability of messenger molecules directing hemoglobin synthesis is the only factor controlling the extent of hemoglobin gene expression during the terminal differentiation of an erythroid clone.

REFERENCES

Attfield, M. (1951). *J. Genet.* **50**, 150.
Bank, A., Rifkind, R. A., and Marks, P. A. (1970). *In* "Regulation of Hematopoiesis" (A. S. Gordon, ed.), Vol. 1, p. 701. Appleton, New York.

Bordin, S., Farace, M. G., and Fantoni, A. (1972). *Biochim. Biophys. Acta* **281**, 277.

Borghese, E. (1969). *Acta Anat.* **36**, 185.

Brawerman, A. S., and Bank, A. (1969). *J. Mol. Biol.* **42**, 57.

Britten, R. J., and Davidson, E. H. (1969). *Science* **165**, 349.

Burka, E. R., and De Bellis, R. (1967). *Nature (London)* **213**, 724.

Burton, K. (1955). *Biochem. J.* **62**, 315.

Chui, D., Djaldetti, M., Marks, P. A., and Rifkind, R. A. (1971). *J. Cell Biol.* **51**, 585.

Conconi, F., Rowley, R. T., Del Senno, L., Pontremoli, S., and Volpato, S. (1972). *Nature (London)* **238**, 83.

Craig, M. L., and Russel, E. S. (1964). *Develop. Biol.* **10**, 191.

Danon, D., and Cividalli, L. (1968). *Biochem. Biophys. Res. Commun.* **30**, 717.

De Bellis, R. (1969). *Biochemistry* **8**, 3451.

de la Chapelle, A., Fantoni, A., and Marks, P. A. (1969). *Proc. Nat. Acad. Sci. U.S.* **63**, 812.

Ebert, J. D., and Kaighn, M. E. (1966). In "Major Problems in Developmental Biology" (M. Locke, ed.), p. 29. Academic Press, New York.

Falvey, A. K., and Staehelin, T. (1970). *J. Mol. Biol.* **53**, 1.

Fantoni, A. (1971). *Protides Biol. Fluids, Proc. Colloq.* **18**, 109.

Fantoni, A., and Bordin, S. (1971). *Biochim. Biophys. Acta* **238**, 245.

Fantoni, A., Bank, A., and Marks, P. A. (1967). *Science* **157**, 1327.

Fantoni, A., de la Chapelle, A., Rifkind, R. A., and Marks, P. A. (1968). *J. Mol. Biol.* **33**, 79.

Fantoni, A., de la Chapelle, A., and Marks, P. A. (1969a). *J. Biol. Chem.* **244**, 75.

Fantoni, A., de la Chapelle, A., Chui, D., Rifkind, R. A., and Marks, P. A. (1969b). *Ann. N.Y. Acad. Sci.* **165**, Art. 1, 194.

Fantoni, A., Ghiara, L., and Pozzi, L. V. (1972a). *Biochim. Biophys. Acta* **269**, 141.

Fantoni, A., Bordin, S., and Lunadei, M. (1972b). *Cell Differentiation* **1**, 219.

Glowackim, E. R., and Millette, J. B. (1965). *J. Mol. Biol.* **11**, 116.

Gurdon, J. B., Lingrel, J. B., and Marbaix, G. (1973). *J. Mol. Biol.* **80**, 539.

Herzberg, M., Revel, M., and Danon, D. (1969). *Eur. J. Biochem.* **11**, 148.

Kovach, J. S., Marks, P. A., Russell, E. S., and Epler, H. (1967). *J. Mol. Biol.* **25**, 131.

Laird, P. (1954). *Exp. Cell Res.* **6**, 30.

Marks, P. A., and Kovach, J. S. (1966). *Curr. Top. Develop. Biol.* **1**, 213.

Marks, P. A., and Rifkind, R. A. (1972). *Science* **175**, 955.

Marks, P. A., Rifkind, R. A., and Danon, D. (1963) *Proc. Natl. Acad. Sci. U.S.* **50**, 356.

Marks, P. A., Fantoni, A., and de la Chapelle, A. (1968). *Vitam. Horm. (New York)* **24**, 331.

Paul, J., and Hunter, J. A. (1968). *Nature (London)* **219**, 1362.

Paul, J., and Hunter, J. A. (1969). *J. Mol. Biol.* **42**, 31.

Perry, R. P., and Kelley, D. E. (1968). *J. Mol. Biol.* **35**, 37.

Perry, R. P., and Kelley, D. E. (1973). *J. Mol. Biol.* **79**, 681.

Rowley, P. T. (1965). *Nature (London)* **208**, 244.

Scheiness, D., and Darnell, J. E. (1973). *Nature (London), New Biol.* **241**, 265.

Schreier, M. H., and Staehelin, T. (1972). *J. Mol. Biol.* **73**, 329.

Singer, M. F., and Leder, P. (1966). *Annu. Rev. Biochem.* **37**, 681.

Singer, R. H., and Penman, S. (1973). *J. Mol. Biol.* **78**, 321.

Spirin, A. S. (1969). *Eur. J. Biochem.* **10**, 20.

Spohr, G., Gramboulan, N., Morel, C., and Scherrer, K. (1970). *Eur. J. Biochem.* **17**, 296.

Terada, M., Banks, J., and Marks, P. A. (1971). *J. Mol. Biol.* **62**, 347.

Terada, M., Cantor, L., Metafora, S., Rifkind, R. A., Bank, A., and Marks, P. A. (1972). *Proc. Nat. Acad. Sci. U.S.* **69**, 3575.

Till, J. E., McCullough, E. A., and Siminovitch, L. (1964). *Proc. Nat. Acad. Sci.* **51**, 29.

Winslow, R. M., and Ingram V. M. (1966). *J. Biol. Chem.* **241**, 1144.

CHAPTER 3

CHANGING POPULATIONS OF REITERATED DNA TRANSCRIPTS DURING EARLY ECHINODERM DEVELOPMENT

H. R. Whiteley and A. H. Whiteley

DEPARTMENTS OF MICROBIOLOGY AND ZOOLOGY AND
THE FRIDAY HARBOR LABORATORIES
UNIVERSITY OF WASHINGTON, SEATTLE, WASHINGTON

I. Introduction

In the intensive analysis that has been made of the timing and regulation of the expression of the genome during the development of the echinoderm, many methods and approaches have been used. While it is possible that the broad events of development are derived from the expression of a *single* or a *few* genes of critical import in the same sense that the phenotypic expression of an inheritable trait is relatable to a gene locus, an alternative possibility is that the major steps of embryonic determination, differentiation, and morphogenesis are brought about by the concerted effects of *many* genes, acting coordinately, triggered by external events or internal clocks. Genetic analysis of stage-specific cistrons and their mutants would be the best means of examining the first possibility, but echinoid early development does not yet lend itself to this approach. The second alternative can be examined by methods that summate the effects of many genes.

We have taken the position that the second alternative is likely and that the first- and second-order events of early embryonic and larval development would be correlated with, and perhaps anticipated by, sizable changes in gene expression. These, we thought, would be revealed in changing populations of primary gene products, titratable by molecular hybridization techniques. Our initial studies (Whiteley *et al.*, 1966), designed for an examination of the most numerous transcripts, revealed clear-cut transcriptional changes during sea urchin development. Similar changes in patterns of transcription were found in the sea urchin by Glisin *et al.* (1966) and in the clawed toad by Denis (1966). It was shortly thereafter determined (Britten and Kohne, 1968) that the products we were measuring with our conditions of annealing were transcripts of repeated DNA sequences of the sea urchin genome. While these include some messages for protein translation, a substantial portion of these transcripts have functions that are still unknown. With further study, additional correlations were found between reiterated sequences and evolutionary relationships (Whiteley *et al.*, 1970). The accumulation of evidence (reviewed by Britten and Davidson, 1969; Darnell *et al.*, 1973; Davidson and Britten, 1973) that much of the RNA derived from reiterated genes is nuclear and that it is included in large molecules interspersed with transcripts of unique DNA sequences reinforces the possibility that the changing populations of repeated DNA transcripts in the urchin embryo are derived from regulatory changes associated with determination and differentiation. We intend, therefore, to review the status of knowledge with respect to activity of genes of moderate level of reiteration in echinoid development.

Initially, however, we wish to consider certain aspects of the genome of the echinoid in order to provide a basis for evaluation of the observations on transcription. This will take the form of a brief summary of the basic parameters of the genome, its sequence organization and the sequence organization of the primary and secondary transcriptional products. This information has been derived from recent literature, and no attempt will be made to consider the evidence on which it is based or to cover all related studies.

II. Organization and Transcription of the Echinoid Genome

A. CHARACTERISTICS OF THE DNA

The chromosomes of echinoids are small, numerous, and cytologically undistinguished. The diploid number for *Strongylocentrotus purpuratus* is 36 (Makino, 1956). The genome size of *S. purpuratus* has been estimated by Hinegardner (1968) to be 0.89 pg a haploid set. That for

Dendraster excentricus has been estimated by relative microspectrophotometry by Brookbank and Cummins (1972) to be 1.22 times that of *S. purpuratus*, or 1.09 pg per haploid set. Neither von Ledebur-Villiger (1972) nor Brookbank and Cummins (1972) report microspectrophotometric values for embryonic cells with more than the 4c amount of DNA.

The kinetic complexity of DNA from echinoid sperm shows no unusual features. C_0t curves (Britten and Kohne, 1968) indicate that some of the DNA reanneals at rates indicating that it contains segments of very low complexity and high levels of reiteration, characteristic of satellite DNA or of internal reverse repeats (Wilson and Thomas, 1974). According to Britten *et al.* (1972), about 38% of *S. purpuratus* DNA, sheared to 450 nucleotide fragments, reassociates with second-order kinetics and can be assumed to be of single-copy sequences. The remainder is made up of repetitive DNA which may consist of various sized families of related sequences or may be dispersed as a continuum of sequences of varying levels of reiteration and without a sharp distinction between repeated and unique DNA (McCarthy and Farquhar, 1972). The measured proportion of the DNA assigned to each class varies with fragment length and annealing conditions; however, one estimate (Graham *et al.*, 1974) for the genome of *S. purpuratus* is given in Table I. The reassocia-

TABLE I

Kinetic Complexity of *Strongylocentrotus purpuratus* DNA[a]

Class of DNA	Frequency of sequence/ genome	Proportion in genome (%)	Kinetic complexity, nucleotide pairs
Nonrepetitive	1	38	3.0×10^8
Repetitive			
Slowly renaturing	20–50	25	1.0×10^7
Moderately fast renaturing	250	27	1.0×10^6
Rapidly renaturing	6000	7	1.3×10^4
Very rapidly renaturing, satellite and internal repeats	—	3	—

[a] Data taken from Graham *et al.* (1974) and Britten *et al.* (1972).

tion curve obtained with *D. excentricus* DNA, a taxonomically distant species, parallels that of *S. purpuratus* except for a slight displacement indicating a slightly greater genome size (S. Mizuno, A. H. Whiteley, and H. R. Whiteley, unpublished observations). The relative proportions of reiterated and unique DNA, however, are very similar.

The linear organization of reiterated and unique sequences in eukaryotic DNA is under analysis for several organisms (Thomas *et al.*, 1974;

Davidson *et al.*, 1973; Bonner and Wu, 1973; Graham *et al.*, 1974; Holmes and Bonner, 1974a,b) and several different models have been proposed (review by Laird, 1973). The evidence derived from studies of *S. purpuratus* DNA (Graham *et al.*, 1974) suggests that reiterated and single-copy sequences are interspersed and that the genome has the following organization: about 6% of the genome consists of tandem repetitive sequences; approximately 50% consists of repetitive units 200–400 nucleotides in average length interspersed with nonrepetitive segments which average 1000 nucleotides in length; about 20% is comprised of repeated sequences 300 nucleotides in length interspersed with single copy sequences at least 3400 nucleotides long; the remaining 22% of the genome may be single-copy DNA, or repetitive sequences interspersed with very long single-copy sequences.

Inverted repeated sequences (palindromes) have been identified in a variety of other eukaryotic DNAs (Wilson and Thomas, 1974). These sequences form hairpin structures 300–1200 nucleotides in length, are present in clusters of 2–4, and are arranged nonrandomly along the chromosome at spacings of 10–80 μm. The function of these structures, which are present with a frequency of many thousands per genome, is unknown. Wilson and Thomas have speculated that they may serve as recognition sites for protein binding to chromatin.

The relationship between these interspersed DNA elements and the cytology of the chromosome is not known in the sea urchin, but in dipteran polytene chromosomes, one visible chromomeric band is believed to represent one gene (Beerman, 1972). In line with this, the moderately repeated DNA has a generalized distribution throughout the chromosomes, based on *in situ* hybridization of *Rhynchosciara* polytene chromosomes (Eckhardt, 1972). The models available (Laird, 1973) provide for an ordered and periodic interspersion of multiple and single-copy DNA in each chromomere in the dipteran chromosome. That the chromomere functions as a single unit, apparently involving both repeated and unique sequences, is indicated by the finding that the primary transcript from Balbiani ring 2 of *Chironomus* is probably a single-sized RNA molecule having a sedimentation constant of 75 S and a molecular weight of 15×10^6. This large molecule ($>$45,000 nucleotides), representing all the Balbiani ring 2 chromomere and including transcript from reiterated DNA sequences, is believed to be responsible for the production of one large protein product (Daneholt and Hosick, 1974; Lambert, 1974).

B. THE NATURE OF THE PRIMARY GENE PRODUCT

In addition to the observations on the primary gene product of the specialized polytenic chromosome cited above, information is accumulat-

ing that the structure of heterogeneous nuclear RNA resembles that described above for DNA, and it has been proposed that translatable messenger RNA (mRNA) is derived from heterogeneous nuclear RNA by
processing (reviewed by Darnell et al., 1973; Georgiev, 1972). A contrary
point of view is discussed by Davidson and Britten (1973). Jelinek et
al. (1974) and Molloy et al. (1974) found that these molecules, ranging
from 5000 to 50,000 nucleotides in length, contain a poly(A) terminus
on the 3' end attached posttranscriptionally to an mRNA segment of
about 3000 nucleotides. The latter is preceded on the 5' end of the molecule by a large segment of rapidly annealing RNA which contains transcripts of reiterated DNA sequences interspersed with less rapidly hydri-
dizing segments. The reiterated segments contain hairpin structures 500
nucleotides in length and also include three short (30 bases) oligo(U)
stretches near the 5' terminus. In the simpler eukaryote *Dictyostelium*,
the heterogeneous nuclear RNA is much smaller but again carries a reiterated sequence transcript of about 300 nucleotides at the 5' end of a
unique mRNA segment (about 1200 nucleotides long), which in turn has
a short (25 nucleotide) poly(A) sequence at the 3' end (Lodish et al.,
1974).

In the sea urchin, the primary gene product is heterogeneous in size
with a predominance of large molecules (Aronson and Wilt, 1969; Hogan
and Gross, 1972; Peltz, 1973); a range of $0.3–3.0 \times 10^6$ molecular weight
has been reported (Kung, 1974). A renaturation analysis of heterogeneous
RNA from sea urchin gastrulae has led Smith et al. (1974) to conclude
that these molecules, or fragments of them, contain repetitive sequence
transcripts of about 300 bases interspersed with larger amounts of single-
copy transcripts. They estimate that 25–100% of the heterogeneous RNAs
show this interspersion. A similar pattern of interspersed repetitive and
unique sequences has been proposed for heterogeneous nuclear RNA in
rat ascites cells (Holmes and Bonner, 1974a,b).

It has been proposed that the translatable nuclear mRNAs appear
in a primary transcript of heterogeneous RNA (Darnell et al., 1973) and,
except for histone mRNAs, that a large proportion contain poly(A) at
the 3' terminus. Prior to their translation, these molecules are cleaved
to release the mRNA. The details and extent of this processing are not
known, but an early event is the adenylylation of the nuclear RNAs at
the 3' terminus (Darnell et al., 1973). Messenger RNA may also undergo
methylation (Perry and Kelly, 1974), but it is not known where or when
this modification occurs. Processing may lead to a rather complete turnover of the bulk of the primary transcript. While this cleavage is believed
to occur mainly in the nucleus, the 75 S primary transcript of Balbiani
ring 2 of *Chironomus* passes nearly intact to the cytoplasm, presumably
to be processed there and the possibility should not be excluded that these

primary transcripts might be processed in the cytoplasm in other special cases. For example, it is well demonstrated that posttranscriptional adenylylation of large RNA molecules occurs in the cytoplasm of activated sea urchin eggs (Slater *et al.*, 1972; Slater and Slater, 1974). The rate of processing is relatively rapid in terms of a cell division time. In the sea urchin, heterogeneous nuclear RNA turns over rapidly (Kijima and Wilt, 1969). The major portion is reported to have a half-time of 7 minutes and a second component, part of which becomes cytoplasmic mRNA, has a half-life of 60–90 minutes (Brandhorst and Humphreys, 1971, 1972).

From their first appearance, the primary transcripts are, for the most part, associated with protein as ribonucleoprotein particles. These were initially described by Spirin from embryos of the loach and shortly thereafter from embryos of the sea urchin (Infante and Nemer, 1968) as cytoplasmic particles (informosomes) containing mRNA in a state intermediate between transcription and translation (reviewed by Spirin, 1969). Similar particles have since been isolated from nuclei of a large variety of cells. The following features concerning them are emerging, based on a few selected recent references (Neyfakh, 1971; Lukanidin *et al.*, 1972; Pederson, 1974; Martin *et al.*, 1974): 80% or more of the newly synthesized RNA appears in these particles and it is proposed that all heterogeneous nuclear RNA primary gene transcripts are so complexed. They sediment at 30 S and appear relatively homogeneous in the electron microscope. The density of the formaldehyde-fixed particles is 1.40 gm/cc, reflecting a protein composition of 75–80%; in contrast, ribosomes have a density of 1.55 gm/cc. These particles have their own set of proteins (informofers) distinct from those associated with polysomal mRNA. A great difference of view exists concerning the heterogeneity of these proteins: Georgiev and his collaborators concluded that there is a single protein subunit, Martin and his associates found two species, others reported multiple components, Pederson found complex populations which are cell specific, and he proposed that different gene primary products are combined with different sets of proteins. It is apparent that the processing of the heterogeneous nuclear RNA is intermixed with the processing of this transport particle. The question of cytoplasmic localization of these particles is ambiguous and whether processing and release of mRNA occurs in the nucleus, in transit through the nuclear envelope, or in the cytoplasm has not been resolved. At least in one instance, the unfertilized sea urchin egg, nontranslatable transcripts exist for prolonged periods, unequivocally in the cytoplasm, in the form of particles with several characteristics similar to those of the 30 S nuclear ribonucleoprotein particles (Spirin, 1969). These characteristics will be described later.

But here also, it is not known whether these cytoplasmic particles have undergone some modification in leaving the nucleus to produce the stable state which permits them to be stored in the cytoplasm until fertilization.

C. MESSENGER RNA

The mRNAs present in eukaryotic polysomes are reported generally to involve transcripts of the nonreiterated part of the genome, except for histone mRNAs. Klein *et al.* (1974) reported that most mRNAs from HeLa cell polysomes, selected by virtue of 3′-poly(A) sequences, complement nonrepetitive DNA sequences and lack associated "tags" of reiterated transcripts. However, at least 6% of the adenylylated mRNA is transcribed entirely from reiterated DNA. Messenger RNA extracted from polysomes of the gastrulae of the sea urchin, *S purpuratus*, has been found by Goldberg *et al.* (1973) and Galau *et al.* (1974) to anneal almost entirely with single-copy DNA. The uncertainty in this estimate is reported to be about 10%, and it is possible that this proportion of the mRNA could be derived from reiterated DNA. Gastrular polysomal RNA, when allowed to react to near completion, is estimated to complex with 2.7% of the sea urchin DNA, which the authors calculate to involve 1.7×10^7 nucleotide pairs, sufficient to encode about 14,000 average polypeptides. Some of these transcripts are doubtless present at higher concentrations than others.

In contrast, Dina *et al.* (1973, 1974) and Crippa *et al.* (1974) reported that RNA molecules isolated from polysomes of *Xenopus* embryos carry a reiterated segment covalently linked to the 5′ end of the single copy informational sequences. The transcript of reiterated DNA is estimated to be 50–60 nucleotides in length, homogeneous in size but of unknown sequence heterogeneity and to have a reiteration frequency of about 2000 copies per diploid genome, somewhat higher than the rRNA cistrons. Their evidence indicates that 75–80% of the poly(A)-containing mRNAs carry such a segment. The majority of the mRNAs of *Dictyostelium* similarly are reported to contain a segment of repetitive sequence transcript on the 5′ end of the molecule (Lodish *et al.*, 1974); the mRNA of insects may also have a short sequence of repetitive RNA (Ilan and Ilan, 1973).

There is, as yet, no convincing demonstration that eukaryotic mRNA in polysomes is polycistronic, although Giudice *et al.* (1972) have reported isolation of giant RNA molecules up to 5×10^7 molecular weight from the cytoplasm of sea urchin gastrulae. As stated earlier, Daneholt and Hosick (1974) have direct evidence of 75 S RNA in the cytoplasm of *Chironomus* salivary gland cells. If heterogeneous nuclear RNA is the precursor to mRNA, it appears that only one mRNA molecule is produced from each precursor, the rest being processed away. Inasmuch as this remainder includes single-copy transcripts as well as multiple copy ones, it would appear that much of the single-copy part of the genome is not informational in the sense of encoding proteins. Therefore, deriving estimates of the number of mRNA molecules or numbers of potential polypeptides from data describing the genetic complexity will provide an overestimate of uncertain magnitude.

If the transcription of unique structural genes is regulated by the reiterated segments, one would expect to find significant changes in both, correlated with developmental events and with evolutionary drifts in the genomes. Qualitatively similar evolutionary divergence has been found in the repeated and nonrepeated sequences of DNA of primates (Kohne, 1970) and *Drosophila* (reviewed by Laird, 1973). A study of the evolution of North American plethodont salamanders (Mizuno and Macgregor, 1974) has shown that there is a clear correspondence between similarity of both the repeated and the unique sequences of the genomes and the taxonomic relatedness in this group. Seemingly, therefore, both regions of the genome may change in a coordinate way.

D. Functions of Reiterated DNA Sequences

Two functions have been established for reiterated DNA: (1) the encoding of the histone proteins and (2) the encoding of the three classes of nontranslated RNAs—tRNA, rRNA, and 5 S RNA. The mRNAs for four of the histone classes (all but the F1 histone) have been isolated from sea urchin embryos (Weinberg *et al.*, 1972) and have an average molecular weight of 1.5×10^5 (9 S). So far as is known, they are exceptional among mRNAs in lacking a 3'-poly(A) segment and being wholly derived from reiterated DNA. The histone cistrons have now been purified from the DNA of *Psammechinus miliaris* by Birnstiel *et al.* (1974), who concluded that this part of the genome is made up of discrete sequences of 2 to 6×10^7 molecular weight and is comprised of mixtures of encoding and spacer segments. Four histone classes, all except F1, are encoded in these closely linked, possibly intermingled, segments which can be completely separated from the tRNA, rRNA, and 5 S RNA cistrons. The buoyant density of the combined histone sequences in CsCl is 1.7036 gm/cc corresponding to 43% G + C. The G + C content of the separated encoding and spacer segments is 51% and 37%, respectively. Histone mRNAs for all four classes are complementary only to the encoding regions. Characteristics of the melting profiles suggest that about one-fourth of the DNA sequences function in coding and one-half as spacer, but the exact proportions are not yet certain. The encoding segments appear to have undergone a small degree of base sequence divergence (about 1–3%) in their evolution whereas the spacer segments appear substantially divergent. All of the four classes of histone cistrons are repeated about 1000 times per genome and comprise 0.5–0.8% of the DNA or, exclusive of spacer, about 0.25% based on a genome size of 0.9 pg of DNA/haploid set in *Psammechinus*. The total histone cistrons in the genome of *S. purpuratus* have a reiteration frequency estimated to be 2000 (McCarthy and Farquhar, 1972).

The cistrons coding for rRNAs in the sea urchin appear as a density satellite in DNA isolated from sperm of *Lytechinus variegatus* (Patterson and Stafford, 1970). The density in CsCl is 1.722 gm/cc corresponding to a $G + C$ content of 63%, compared with 1.695 gm/cc and a 35% $G + C$ content for the main part of the DNA. Ribosomal RNA hybridizes only with this satellite DNA; the saturation level is 0.37 µg rRNA/µg rDNA (Patterson and Stafford, 1971). The sedimentation coefficients for rRNAs of *Arbacia punctulata* have been determined by Sy and McCarty (1968) to be 18 S and 26 S. A small RNA species has been extracted from the 26 S subunit, employing denaturing conditions. This small species has a sedimentation coefficient of 5.8, contains approximately 150 nucleotides, and has a molecular weight of about 50,000 (Sy and McCarty, 1970, 1971). The precursor of rRNAs of *Paracentrotus lividus* is apparently transcribed as a molecule sedimenting with a value of 33 S, corresponding to a molecular weight of 2.58 $\times 10^6$ (Sconzo *et al.*, 1971). This molecule is methylated and processed to the 18 S subunit with a molecular weight of 0.68 $\times 10^6$ and a precursor of 28 S (1.58 $\times 10^6$ molecular weight), which is also methylated. A portion of molecular weight 0.33 $\times 10^6$ is discarded in this step. The 28 S precursor is processed at a rate about one-fifth that of the first step to produce the mature 26 S subunit (molecular weight of 1.4 $\times 10^6$) and a fragment of 0.18 $\times 10^6$, which is discarded. These observations indicate that the events of processing are similar to those of other poikilothermic animals. The reiteration frequency for the 26 S rRNA, determined by Sy and McCarty (1970), is about 200 gene copies, representing 0.057% of the sperm DNA. The 5.8 S rRNA which they find hydrogen-bonded to the 26 S molecule saturates 0.003–0.004% of the DNA, corresponding to 300–400 gene copies. Mutolo and Giudice (1967) have found that 0.03% of the genome of *Paracentrotus lividus* is complementary to rRNA.

Little information exists concerning the nature of the genes coding for 5 S ribosomal RNA and the tRNAs in sea urchins.

The functions of the remainder, and major portion, of the reiterated DNA are not known. Highly reiterated (satellite) DNA has generally been found in centromeric heterochromatin (reviewed by Eckhardt, 1972). This DNA is not transcribed and is subject to rapid evolutionary change (Flamm *et al.*, 1969). The highly reiterated DNA of sea urchins has not been studied extensively but presumably would have the same functions as in other organisms.

Several models have been proposed based on the idea that the moderately reiterated sequences function to regulate transcription and are not merely spacer or completely nonfunctional segments of the DNA. The sequence organization of DNA and of heterogeneous nuclear RNA and the predominantly nuclear localization of transcripts of repeated sequences provide the major support for these models. Britten and Davidson (1969, 1972) have proposed that transcripts of repeated DNA activate batteries of structural genes. Georgiev (1969, 1972), on the other hand, argues that reiterated segments function as binding sites for repressors, thereby regulating transcription of large portions of the DNA; the large transcripts are then processed to yield one or more mRNA molecules. The processing of mRNA and posttranscriptional modification can also be viewed as regulatory processes, possibly involving reiterated segments (Darnell et al., 1973). Each of these models has attractive features but definitive experiments establishing the role of the reiterated transcripts have not yet been performed, and it should be kept in mind that some multiple copy RNA is present in polysomes and that transcripts of reiterated sequences may have a *number* of functions.

One of the several possible functions which might be envisaged for transcripts of repeated DNA is that of association with proteins. The observations that heterogeneous RNA is complexed with proteins (informofers) presumably for transport and/or protection against premature translation, implies the existence of recognition sites; the formation of protein–RNA complexes could involve the nonmRNA segments of the primary transcript. If the high levels of cellular specificity reported by Pederson (1974) for these proteins proves to be general, then there may be correlated changes in populations of the nonmessage combining sites.

The presence and structural organization of reiterated DNA transcripts in heterogeneous nuclear RNA suggests the possibility that they could also regulate processing, assuming that heterogeneous RNA is the precursor of mRNA. It might be speculated that the hairpin regions, in particular, could serve as recognition points for specific nucleases involved in selective degradation of precursor molecules. Other possible posttranscriptional controls have been discussed by Darnell et al. (1973). Finally, if mRNAs do, in fact, have a small segment of reiterated transcript at the 5′ end, this portion of the molecule might play a role in the translational process. Thus, reiterated DNA transcripts could function at several key steps of gene expression, thereby affecting events of development. Not all of these would require a high level of specificity in nucleotide sequences in the RNAs but orderly and consistent, temporally specific changes in such RNA populations in certain cells and at key developmental stages could find their interpretation in terms of regulation of gene function and specification of important sets of proteins.

III. Reiterated DNA Transcripts in Echinoid Development

A. CONSIDERATION OF METHODS

The hybridization experiments reviewed in the following sections were undertaken specifically to measure the reactions of reiterated sequences. As detailed above, these sequences make up a significant part of the echinoderm genome and, except for a few specific genes, their function has not been established. Since echinoderm DNA has a relatively low proportion of *highly* reiterated segments (Table I), and these seem generally not to be transcribed, the reactions that we have measured probably involve *moderately* reiterated or "intermediate repetitive" DNA (reviewed by Walker, 1971). However, we have not distinguished between the contributions of highly reiterated sequences and the moderately repeated ones and will, therefore, refer to these parts of the genome and their transcripts simply as "reiterated sequences." Control experiments show that rRNA and tRNA are not significantly involved in our hybridization reactions. The problems and limitations, as well as the advantages, inherent in the hybridization method and in the use of immobilized DNA have been discussed elsewhere (McCarthy and McConaughy, 1968; Church and McCarthy, 1968; McCarthy and Church, 1970; Paul, 1970; Kennell, 1971).

Most of our experiments have been performed at low RNA/DNA ratios (0.08–2.0) in order to emphasize RNAs present in the embryo at relatively high frequency. We assume that these transcripts will have at least a quantitatively significant function; no attempt has been made to measure the rare multiple-copy transcripts nor the proportion of the DNA which has been expressed. We have relied on stringent conditions of temperature (16 hours at 66–68°) and salt concentration (0.3 M NaCl–0.03 M sodium citrate) plus ribonuclease treatment to minimize base-pair mismatching. The fidelity of base pairing has been reasonably good as judged by the steeply rising melting curves and T_m values; the latter have indicated 4–6% base-pair mismatching (based on Ullman and McCarthy, 1973) in RNA–DNA and DNA–DNA duplexes. Unless specified otherwise, RNA has been extracted from whole cells or embryos and represents, therefore, a mixture of heterogeneous nuclear and cytoplasmic components. This RNA is heterogeneous in gradient centrifugation and acrylamide gel electrophoresis and contains polyadenylylated molecules as determined by retention on Millipore filters (Lee *et al.*, 1971). Depending on the RNA/DNA ratios, 6–20% of the input H^3-RNA has been hybridized, except in experiments where noted.

Many of the experiments involve competition–hybridization, which has been assayed by the following methods: (1) mixing labeled and unlabeled RNAs together and reacting these with filter-bound DNA; (2) "sequential annealing" (incubating unlabeled RNA with immobilized DNA, removing unreacted RNA and adding labeled RNA in a second step of incubation; Whiteley et al., 1966), and (3) "additivity experiments" (using a high concentration of one RNA plus varying concentrations of another RNA in order to determine if the two RNAs contained the same or different populations; Whiteley et al., 1970). These experiments have been carried out to a concentration of 3–6 mg/ml total competitor RNA to approach a plateau level. In addition, the double-reciprocal plot of Hansen et al. (1970; Spiegelman et al., 1975) has been used to extrapolate the level of competition to an infinite concentration of competitor (Whiteley et al., 1975), thus permitting a more objective evaluation and confirmation of the differences between different preparations. Similarly, data obtained in saturation experiments have been reanalyzed by the Scatchard plot (Marsh and McCarthy, 1973) to confirm conclusions based on the estimation of the level of saturation at infinite concentration of labeled RNA.

B. Egg RNA

During oogenesis, the echinoid egg is supplied with a high concentration of RNA, sufficient in quantity and informational content to permit development to an irregular blastula (Harvey, 1940). Much of the RNA of the ovum is ribosomal and transfer RNA. The remainder, estimated as 3–4% of the total egg RNA (Slater and Spiegelman, 1966, 1968) is present as a heterogeneous array of molecules which are inactive in protein synthesis, probably because they are complexed with protein (informosomes). Thus, the unfertilized egg has a low level of protein synthesis (Nakano and Monroy, 1958; Epel, 1967) and contains few free or bound polysomes as detected by electron micrography (Sachs and Anderson, 1970) and sedimentation analyses (Rinaldi and Monroy, 1969). Most of this RNA, which we will call "egg" or "egg-type" RNA (also called "maternal RNA" by others) must be located in the cytoplasm. The egg has a small, nonbasophilic pronucleus which electron micrographs (Longo, 1972) show to contain few ribonucleoprotein particles. Also, enucleated merogones have been demonstrated to have translatable RNA (Denny and Tyler, 1964) and RNA which is adenylylated after fertilization (Wilt, 1973).

Additional evidence supporting the cytoplasmic and particulate local-

ization of egg RNA comes from competition-hybridization experiments
(Whiteley *et al.*, 1975). RNA was extracted from unfertilized eggs and
from heavy and light merogones obtained by centrifugation of *D. excentricus* eggs. As shown in Fig. 1A, all three RNA preparations were effec-

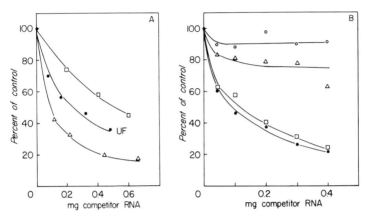

FIG. 1. Competition by RNA extracted from fractions of unfertilized eggs of
Dendraster excentricus in the binding of ^{3}H-labeled 1–16-cell RNA to DNA. (A) Competition by RNA from unfertilized eggs (●), light (△) and heavy (□) merogones.
Preparation of merogones and the conditions used in the hybridization reaction have
been described by Whiteley *et al.* (1975). (B) Competition by RNA from fractions of
homogenized unfertilized eggs. Hybridization reactions were performed as described
by Mizuno *et al.* (1973); 22P (△), 105P (□), and 105S (○) refer to particulate (P)
and supernatant (S) fractions resulting from centrifugation at 22,000 or 105,000 rpm.
"Total" (●) refers to the homogenate prior to centrifugation. From Whiteley *et al.*
(1975).

tive competitors in the hybridization of *D. excentricus* DNA and ^{3}H-
labeled RNA extracted from embryos continuously labeled from the 1-
to 16-cell stage. Competition by RNA from the heavy merogones, which
lack the female pronucleus and are much smaller, can be explained only
on the ground that the competing RNA populations are cytoplasmic
rather than nuclear. The particulate localization of the competing molecules can be demonstrated by similar assays using RNA extracted from
large particulates sedimented at 22,000 *g* for 20 minutes and smaller particulates sedimented at 105,000 *g* for 10 hours. Figure 1B shows that the
maximum competition was observed with RNA extracted from the
smaller particulate material and that the extent of this competition was
equal to that seen with RNA from the total unfertilized egg homogenate.
The small amount of competition observed with RNA extracted from
the larger particulates may have been due to contamination by the
22,000 *g* supernatant.

The informational nature of egg RNA has been inferred from the pioneer work of Harvey (1940) and from subsequent enucleation experiments (Ficq and Brachet, 1963; Denny and Tyler, 1964) and inhibitor studies (Gross and Cousineau, 1963). However, few specific proteins have, as yet, been identified as oogenetic in origin. The hybridization experiments of Farquhar and McCarthy (1973) showed that histone mRNA was present in egg RNA. Skoultchi and Gross (1973) confirmed this observation and demonstrated that the histone mRNAs are complexed with protein in particles that sediment at about 25–50 S. RNA from these particles can be translated *in vitro* to produce proteins that coelectrophorese with histones; unidentified polypeptides of different sizes are also produced (Gross *et al.*, 1973). Egg RNA also contains mRNAs coding for tubulins (Raff *et al.*, 1971, 1972; Raff, 1975) and ribonucleotide reductase (Noronha *et al.*, 1972; DePetrocellis *et al.*, 1974). Some evidence has also been presented that mRNA coding for the hatching enzyme may be present in egg RNA (Barrett and Angelo, 1969).

C. RNA Synthesis after Fertilization

Although an extremely low level of RNA synthesis has been detected in unfertilized echinoderm eggs (Levner, 1974), synthesis of this macromolecule really becomes measurable only after fertilization (Nemer, 1967; Wilt, 1970; Eckberg and Ozaki, 1972; von Ledebur-Villiger, 1972; Mizuno *et al.*, 1973). In the sea urchin, *S. purpuratus*, there is a marked increase in the rate of RNA synthesis after the 16-cell stage (Wilt, 1970) although this involves an actual decrease per nucleus during active cleavage (Eckberg and Ozaki, 1972). In *D. excentricus* (Mizuno *et al.*, 1973), the predominant increase in the rate of incorporation of uridine-^{3}H into RNA begins with the 64-cell stage and continues until after the blastula has hatched.

Synthesis of tRNAs and 5 S RNA (Emerson and Humphreys, 1970; O'Melia and Villee, 1972), as well as end labeling of tRNAs (Glisin and Glisin, 1964), begins soon after fertilization. Emerson and Humphreys (1970) proposed that synthesis of rRNA also begins early in cleavage, but work by other investigators (Comb *et al.*, 1965; Giudice and Mutolo, 1967; Hartman and Comb, 1969; Slater and Spiegelman, 1970; Sconzo and Giudice, 1971) indicates that rRNA is not produced until the blastula or early gastrula stage. Cytological studies agree with the biochemical evidence favoring differential repression of these cistrons during cleavage. Thus, the egg pronucleus and early cleavage nuclei contain one or more nucleolus-bodies which have only the fibrillar component. These bodies do not stain for RNA and do not synthesize RNA as judged from autoradiograms (Karasaki, 1968; Millonig *et al.*, 1968; Emerson and Humphreys, 1971; Longo, 1972). However, typical bipartite nucleoli appear in late blastulae coincident with radioautographic evidence for RNA synthesis (Karasaki, 1968; Millonig et al., 1968). It is worthy of note that synthesis of 5 S RNA, which usually is coordinate with the 26 S and 18 S species, is activated very much earlier in the urchin.

Some of the RNA produced after insemination can be detected in polysomes and is probably, therefore, messenger RNA (Rinaldi and Monroy, 1969). Two lines of evidence indicate that RNA newly synthesized after fertilization contains histone mRNAs: (1) labeled 9 S RNA can be detected in the small polysomes, which are known to produce histones (Nemer and Lindsay, 1969; Kedes and Gross, 1969), and this RNA has been shown to be histone messenger (Gross et al., 1973); (2) interspecies echinoid hybrids synthesize the paternal form of the F1 histone which, obviously, could not be produced from stored egg RNA (Easton et al., 1974). Thus, histones (D. T. Lindsay, personal communication; Ruderman et al., 1974) and also tubulins (Raff et al., 1972; Raff, 1975) are apparently produced concurrently from preformed and newly transcribed RNA during early cleavage. Polysomes of all sizes contain newly synthesized RNA soon after fertilization (Rinaldi and Monroy, 1969), but it is not known how many proteins produced by these polysomes are encoded by the newly made mRNA and/or egg RNA.

Histone mRNA does not contain the stretches of poly(A) characteristic of most mRNAs (Darnell, 1973). In Lytechinus pictus, an estimated 0.032% of the egg RNA molecules have been determined to be adenylylated with approximately 100 nucleotide residues/molecule (Slater and Slater, 1972; Slater et al., 1973; Wilt, 1973). Most of these RNAs are on cytoplasmic ribonucleoprotein particles (<56 S in size). Shortly after fertilization, there is a transposition of sequences containing poly(A) from these particles to a ribosomal fraction, followed, during the first two cleavages, by an abrupt doubling of the proportion of RNA which is adenylylated. The latter involves addition of 200 adenyl residues to stored egg RNA sequences and occurs in the cytoplasm; these residues are associated mainly with the subribosomal fraction. Subsequent changes are reported not to occur until gastrulation, so the increase is unique to fertilization. Slater and Slater (1972, 1974) and Slater et al. (1973) have interpreted their results to mean that the egg contains both adenylylated and nonadenylylated RNA, that addition of poly(A) occurs after fertilization, and that adenylylated molecules are recruited to ribosomes from subribosomal particles directly or after addition of poly(A). These changes are associated, but not exactly correlated with the activation of protein synthesis. Many of these findings have been confirmed by Wilt (1973), except that in his preparations the poly(A)-containing RNAs are mainly associated with ribosomes. As stated earlier, Wilt also finds that parthenogenesis will induce these changes (1973).

We have used the technique of competition-hybridization to investigate two additional problems concerning the transcripts of reiterated sequences characteristic of the unfertilized eggs: (1) are such transcripts present in RNAs extracted from embryos at various stages of development and (2) is their synthesis renewed and continued at different stages of development (Mizuno *et al.*, 1973; Whiteley *et al.*, 1975). The first question was studied using RNA-^{3}H extracted from sand dollar embryos continuously labeled from the 1- to the 16-cell stage. This RNA was considered to be very similar to reiterated DNA transcripts from the unfertilized eggs on the basis of competition–hybridization experiments, such as those shown in Fig. 1 and, specifically, in Fig. 2. The latter figure

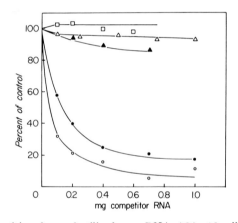

FIG. 2. Competition by unfertilized egg RNA (●), 16-cell stage RNA (○), tRNA (△), rRNA (▲), and poly(A) (□) in the binding of ^{3}H-labeled 1–16-cell RNA to DNA. From Mizuno *et al.* (1973).

indicates that RNAs extracted from 16-cell stage embryos and unfertilized eggs have nearly the same ability to act as competitors in the annealing of the labeled reference RNA. Control experiments with purified RNAs established that hybridization did not involve newly synthesized ribosomal or transfer RNA molecules. Similar experiments with a commercial preparation of poly(A) (determined to be 5 S by gradient sedimentation) showed that the hybridization did not occur through poly(A) stretches.

It is known that transcription of mitochondrial DNA begins shortly after fertilization or parthenogenetic activation (Hartman and Comb, 1969; Craig, 1970; Chamberlain, 1970; Selvig *et al.*, 1972; Chamberlain and Metz, 1972). Based on ethidium bromide sensitivity, an estimated 50–80% of RNA synthesized in early cleavage consists of mitochondrial transcripts (Craig and Piatigorsky, 1971; Chamberlain and Metz, 1972). This synthesis can be detected 40 minutes after fertilization (Selvig *et al.*, 1972), and the products form distinct size classes between 11 S and 17 S (Chamberlain and Metz, 1972). To determine whether mitochondrial transcripts participated in the hybridization reactions illustrated in Fig. 2, comparisons were made of the ability of the labeled reference RNA to anneal to DNA extracted from sperm heads lacking mitochondria and to DNA extracted from intact sand dollar sperm. No differences were found in the binding of the labeled reference RNA to the two DNA preparations, indicating that mitochondrial transcripts did not contribute in a major way to the hybridization reaction.

The T_m of the RNA–DNA duplexes formed with the ^{3}H-labeled 1–16-cell RNA was found to be 78.5°C; for comparison, the T_m of repetitive DNA–DNA duplexes (C_0t 200 material) is 70.5°C, and native sand dollar DNA, determined optically, is 85.4°C. Thermal dissociation of the above ^{3}H-labeled RNA–DNA duplexes revealed two regions in the melting curves. One, accounting for approximately 55% of the radioactivity, was dissociated at temperatures below 80°C (i.e., in the melting range of repetitive DNA–DNA hybrids) whereas the remainder dissociated between 80° and 90°C. This higher melting component may reflect the presence of histone mRNA in the labeled reference RNA since RNA–DNA duplexes containing histone mRNA have been reported to have a T_m of 84–88°C (Kedes and Birnstiel, 1971; McCarthy and Farquhar, 1972) and histone DNA cistrons melt at 85°C (Birnstiel *et al.*, 1974). These families of reiterated sequences yield well-matched duplexes because of the high level of concentration of the histone cistrons, which are relatively conservative in their base sequences (McCarthy and Farquhar, 1972).

The ^{3}H-labeled RNA used in these experiments gave a heterogeneous sedimentation pattern in a sucrose gradient (Mizuno *et al.*, 1973). Although relatively high concentrations of molecules having sedimentation constants typical of mitochondrial RNA (11–17 S), histone mRNA (9–11 S), and tRNA (4 S) were present, the preparations contained RNA sedimenting throughout the range of 4 S to >30 S, and competition experiments with pooled gradient fractions indicated that molecules from the entire range of sizes participated in the hybridization. A similar heterogeneous distribution with numerous components ranging from 2.5×10^5 to 1.5×10^6 molecular weight (Slater and Spiegelman, 1970) was found by acrylamide gel electrophoresis of RNA from *S. purpuratus* continuously labeled from the 1- to 16-cell stage. It is of interest, also, that the trace amounts of RNA synthesized by unfertilized eggs of *L. pictus* (Levner,

1974) displayed a very heterogeneous array of sedimentation constants. Since most of the RNA transcribed from repeated DNA sequences is known to remain in the nucleus (Greenberg and Perry, 1971; Goldberg et al., 1973; Smith et al., 1974), it would be anticipated that much of the ³H-labeled 1–16 cell RNA used in these experiments would be heterogeneous nuclear RNA. On the other hand, Hynes et al. (1972b) found that the RNA synthesized and released to the cytoplasm during metaphase at the 16-cell stage included a broad size spectrum and these species were very stable: their sedimentation pattern remained unchanged for a prolonged time in cells prevented from reentering telophase by the addition of colchicine. Thus, the ³H-labeled 1–16-cell RNA used in our studies may contain both this stable heterogeneous cytoplasmic RNA as well as rapidly turning over heterogeneous nuclear RNA.

In summary, RNA transcribed from reiterated sequences during the first four cleavages has the following properties: (1) it is very similar in base sequence to egg RNA on the basis of competition–hybridization experiments; (2) it is nuclear in origin rather than mitochondrial; (3) it contains populations of molecules which are heterogeneous in size; (4) RNA–DNA duplexes containing this RNA yield a thermal dissociation profile with two components; (5) it probably includes histone mRNAs as one of its components; and (6) although tRNA, mitochondrial RNA, and poly(A) are probably synthesized during the first four cleavages, these species and stretches of poly(A) do not account for the hybridization of ³H-labeled 1–16-cell RNA.

Using ³H-labeled 1–16-cell RNA as a probe, egg-type RNA was found

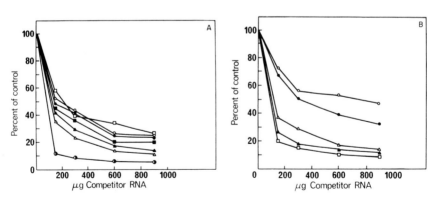

FIG. 3. Competition by RNAs from unfertilized eggs and various developmental stages in the binding of ³H-labeled 1–16-cell RNA to DNA. (A) □, 2-cell; ○, unfertilized egg; ●, zygote; ■, 4-cell; ▲, 8-cell; △, 16-cell; ◐, unhatched blastula. (B) ○, late prism; ●, early prism; △, mid-gastrula; ▲, early gastrula; □, mesenchyme blastula. From Mizuno et al. (1973).

in embryos at all stages of development (Fig 3), but in varying proportions. An estimate of these proportions can be made by comparing the extent of competition at a selected concentration of RNA (Fig. 4). On this basis, a large enrichment of egg-type RNA is apparent during early stages with a maximum in hatching blastulae, followed by a decrease

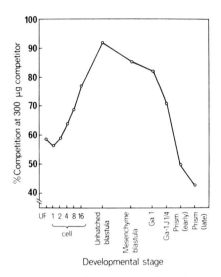

Developmental stage

FIG. 4. Comparison of the relative concentration of competing RNA extracted from embryos of different stages. The hybridization system was ^{3}H-labeled 1–16-cell RNA annealed to *Dendraster excentricus* DNA; comparisons were made at 300 µg competitor RNA; Ga-1 is a beginning gastrula; GaJ-$\frac{1}{4}$ is an embryo that is one-fourth gastrulated. Taken from Mizuno *et al.* (1973).

in older embryos. This pattern of accumulation of egg-type RNA parallels that for the rates of RNA synthesis during early development, both of which increase to a maximum at blastulation. Thereafter, total RNA synthesis remains high while egg-type RNA synthesis declines.

The augmentation in the relative amount of egg-type RNA can be explained most readily on the basis of renewed synthesis of RNAs produced during oogenesis. Direct evidence in support of such renewed and continued synthesis came from competition-hybridization experiments using ^{3}H-labeled RNAs extracted from labeled blastulae, gastrulae, and prisms. RNA from unfertilized eggs was an effective competitor in the annealing of all three ^{3}H-labeled RNAs (Fig. 5) confirming earlier conclusions (Whiteley *et al.*, 1966; Glisin *et al.*, 1966; Hynes and Gross, 1972) that egg-type RNAs are synthesized throughout development. When reference RNAs from 16-cell stage (Fig. 2), blastulae, gastrulae, and prisms (Fig. 5) are tested, it is apparent that the transcription in

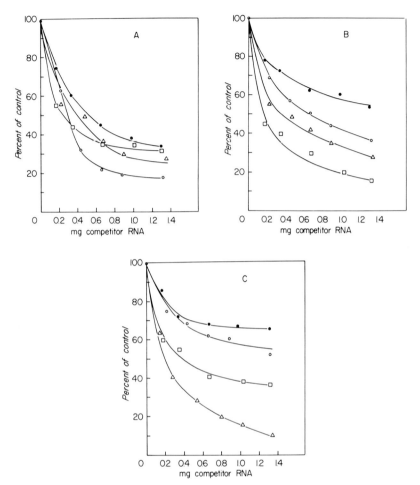

Fig. 5. Competition by RNAs from *Dendraster excentricus* unfertilized eggs (●), blastulae (○), gastrulae (□), and prisms (△) in the binding of three labeled RNAs to DNA. ³H-labeled RNA from (A) hatched blastulae, (B) mid-gastrulae, and (C) prisms. RNA was extracted after 1 hour of labeling of embryos with uridine-³H; all competition experiments were performed as described by Mizuno *et al.* (1973) using RNA/DNA ratios of 0.2–0.4.

the early stages is predominantly of egg-type sequences, with increased emphasis on other sequences in the later stages. The transcription of stage-specific sequences is clearly detectable by the hatching blastula stage (Fig. 5) and will be discussed later.

Kafiani and his associates (Kafiani, 1970) found a different situation with respect to transcription of egg-type RNA in the loach. While the RNA from the unfertilized egg has a good deal of homology with that synthesized in gastrulae and later, they reported a large degradation of these species during cleavage, reaching a minimum in midblastula. There is then a very rapid restoration of these species, correlated with the onset of the most active phase of RNA synthesis.

The presence in the egg of multiple copy RNA which will be carried over into early development has been found for a number of organisms: sea urchins and sand dollars, *Xenopus* (Crippa *et al.*, 1967), *Acmaea* (Karp and Whiteley, 1973), oyster (McLean and Whiteley, 1974), a tubiculous polychaete (Y. R. Lee, personal communication), and the loach (Kafiani, 1970). In all but *Xenopus* (Denis, 1966), transcription of these sequences is renewed after fertilization, and in the echinoid this renewed synthesis leads to a substantial augmentation of these species. A relatively large proportion of transcripts in the early developmental stages has been found to be derived from the repeated sequences with an increased emphasis on unique transcription after the onset of differentiation. Such a pattern has been reported for the loach (Kafiani, 1970) and the mouse (Schultz and Church, 1974), and in *Xenopus* there is a larger amount of repeated, than of unique, DNA represented in the oocyte RNA (Davidson and Hough, 1971; Hough and Davidson, 1972).

The echinoid can develop to a blastulalike stage, but not beyond it, in the absence of nuclear activity whereas limpet and oyster can develop still further even though transcription is restricted. It is possible that entirely normal development during cleavage may require supplementation of egg-type RNA even though the unfertilized eggs contain sufficient copies to support development to a blastulalike stage. The role of these transcripts may be to provide or to regulate the synthesis of messages for generalized cellular functions, such as histone and tubulin synthesis and other "housekeeping" roles (Whiteley *et al.*, 1966). It is conceivable that the rapid production of new unspecialized cells would require both a supply of preestablished components and the provision for the generation of more. The maintenance and repair of these generalized features and the provision for the fewer cell divisions that do occur during gastrulation and prism stages would require fewer of these components and a correspondingly lessened synthesis of the egg-type RNAs needed to generate them. It is also possible that this supplementation is in anticipation of events after blastulation.

The mechanism for reactivation of the DNA sequences which produce these transcripts has not been studied. Possibly these sequences are repressed in a gene-specific way at the termination of oogenesis and are derepressed as part of the egg activation process. This behavior would leave open the question of why these particular sequences are temporarily shut down to be reactivated without even an intervening cell division.

Another possibility is that transcription of sequences during oogenesis may be only temporarily interrupted or greatly diminished during oocyte maturation because of compartmentalization of the substrates or enzymes or compaction of the chromatin. Thus, after fertilization when the egg is reenergized and the interphase nucleus is reestablished, transcription could be renewed without any changes in specific gene regulation. Stage-specific transcription could then occur as the result of the activation of new gene sequences, initially, as shown below, in 16-cell stage micromeres and more extensively at hatching, thus providing populations of new specialized transcripts supplementing the generalized ones already being made.

D. Sixteen-Cell Stage Blastomeres

Although the echinoid ovum lacks morphologically distinguishing features, it has a fixed animal–vegetal polarity (Morgan, 1927) and is determined along its primary axis as shown by Hörstadius (1939). The first morphological differentiation occurs at the fourth cleavage which yields four macromeres, eight mesomeres, and four micromeres. The fates of these cells have already been determined (reviewed by Okazaki, 1975; Timourian, 1975; Spiegel and Spiegel, 1975; Whiteley et al., 1975). The process of determination of each class of blastomeres presumably arises from ooplasmic segregation of cytoplasmic components.

Despite the fact that the development of many kinds of eggs involves ooplasmic segregation, the cytoplasmic components that are segregated and the mechanisms involved remain unknown. If informational molecules play a role in this process, two models could be proposed: (1) specific populations of preformed RNA molecules could be segregated into specific blastomeres, or (2) cytoplasmic "factors" could be segregated into specific blastomeres; if these factors could activate specific genes, there would be a differential synthesis of RNA populations in the different blastomeres. Thus, if the first mechanism were operating, there would be differences in the distribution of egg-type RNA to isolated blastomeres; if the second mechanism were functioning, the blastomeres might synthesize different populations of RNA. These two alternatives were tested by determining the segregation of egg-type RNAs in isolated blastomeres and by comparing the kinds of RNA synthesized by blastomeres at the 16-cell stage.

Blastomeres were fractionated on a sucrose–seawater step gradient (Mizuno et al., 1974) to give preparations of pure sand dollar micromeres and a mixture of meso- plus macromeres; the latter fraction was free of micromeres. The isolated blastomeres were viable and capable of synthesizing RNA at rates which were comparable to that of the intact 16-cell stage embryos. The latter observation is in agreement with the findings of Hynes *et al.* (1972b) and Spiegel and Rubenstein (1972) that isolated 16-cell blastomeres are all able to incorporate labeled uridine but is in opposition to the reports of Czihak (1965) and Czihak and Hörstadius (1970). These investigators reported, on the basis of radioautography, that the micromeres of the 16-cell stage are more active in RNA synthesis than the other blastomeres. The explanation offered by Hynes *et al.* (1972b) seems to account for this discrepancy—that the larger cells may have been in a nontranscriptional phase of the cell cycle when these embryos were prepared for radioautography. Thus, we conclude that all three blastomeres are quantitatively equal in transcription.

If the egg-type RNA populations capable of hybridizing were distributed randomly to each class of blastomeres, RNA extracted from such blastomeres would be expected to compete equally in hybridization experiments. Figure 6 shows, in such an experiment, that no marked differ-

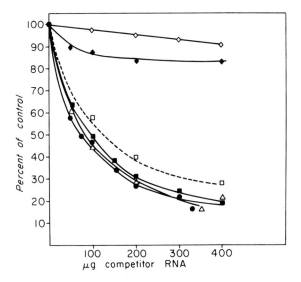

FIG. 6. Competition by RNA from 16-cell stage embryos ($\triangle$), micromeres ($\bullet$), meso plus macromeres ($\blacksquare$), and unfertilized eggs ($\square$) in the binding of ³H-labeled 1–16-cell RNA, including transfer ($\diamond$) and ribosomal ($\blacklozenge$) RNA controls. From Mizuno *et al.* (1974).

ences were found in the distribution of egg-type RNA to the two fractions. Thus, these experiments fail to support the idea that ooplasmic segregation results in the differential distribution of preformed RNAs but do not contradict the second proposed mechanism.

For examination of the second mechanism, 16-cell stage embryos were pulse-labeled for 30 minutes, the blastomeres were separated, and RNA was extracted from micromeres and from meso- plus macromeres. Com-

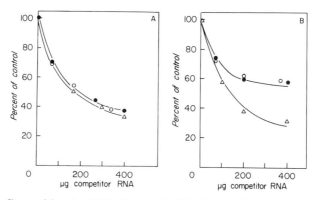

FIG. 7. Competition by RNA from unfertilized eggs (●, ○) and 16-cell stage embryos (△) in the binding of pulse-labeled blastomere RNAs to DNA. (A) ^{3}H-labeled meso- plus macromere RNA. (B) ^{3}H-labeled micromere RNA. Data taken from Mizuno et al. (1974).

petition–hybridization experiments with these preparations (Fig. 7A) gave no evidence for the synthesis of different populations of RNA by the meso- plus macromere fraction (i.e., nearly identical competition curves were obtained with RNAs from unfertilized eggs and the 16-cell stage embryos). In contrast, parallel experiments with ^{3}H-labeled RNA from micromeres showed that unfertilized egg RNA was a less efficient competitor than RNA from total 16-cell stage embryos as shown by the higher plateau level (Fig. 7B). Therefore, the micromere fraction contained newly synthesized RNA molecules transcribed from reiterated DNA sequences which were different from the RNA populations being transcribed by the meso- plus macromeres and not appreciably represented in unfertilized eggs. These experiments support the second mechanism proposed to account for the consequences of ooplasmic segregation—i.e., the distribution to blastomeres of cytoplasmic "factors" capable of influencing qualitatively the synthesis of RNA.

Overall, these experiments demonstrate that although there is no segregation of egg-type transcripts of reiterated sequences among the blastomeres, the micromeres of the 16-cell stage are apparently induced to transcribe different sequences well before the characteristic phenotypic expressions of these cells are revealed. The only related observation is that of Hynes et al. (1972a), who have indirect evidence that the mRNAs for microtubular proteins are not quantitatively segregated among the blastomeres at the fourth cleavage. It is not known whether these RNAs are derived from reiterated genes. Micromeres and meso- plus macromeres dissociated at this time synthesize tubular proteins equally. When cultured, both cell populations increase their relative rate of synthesis of the proteins, the larger cells more than the smaller. It is not known whether this is due to a different rate of transcription of the mRNA for tubular protein in the micromeres and meso- macromeres.

Clearly, blastomeres at the fourth cleavage are highly determined or programmed, at least to an extent equivalent to that of blastomeres of typically mosaic embryos. Isolated micromeres are able to carry out their usual differentiation to produce spicules (Okazaki, 1975), isolated micromeres, and meso- plus macromeres do not reaggregate in the same patterns (Hynes et al., 1972a; Spiegel and Spiegel, 1975), and only the meso-plus macromere fraction is able to develop cilia (Raff, 1972). Blastomeres cultivated in isolation from the 16-cell stage are programmed to initiate rRNA and tRNA synthesis 24 and 48 hours later, approximately on normal schedule (Hynes et al., 1972b). The qualitative changes in transcription of reiterated sequences at the 16-cell stage which are shown in Fig. 7 may, in some unknown manner, reflect an early event in the establishment of the pattern of determination.

These observations permit the definition of some technically difficult problems but ones of a good deal of significance. Do these cell-specific transcripts regulate the synthesis of proteins *specific* to the differentiative events of micromeres? Do they regulate *sets* of genetic functions? Are they maintained from the 16-cell stage until posthatching in an unexpressed state or do they begin to function without delay? If they are stored, what later event activates them? What is the molecular nature of the component(s) responsible for the activation of the micromere nuclei? What mechanism exists for sorting these out, presumably from the cytoplasm specifically into the micromere nuclei?

E. REITERATED TRANSCRIPTS IN BLASTULAE, GASTRULAE, AND PRISM LARVAE

Our initial experiments (Whiteley et al., 1966) on the populations of RNA present in S. purpuratus at different stages of development were of two types: (1) competition–hybridization and (2) sequential hybridization, as described earlier. Both types of experiments gave the same results: i.e., different populations of RNA molecules were present in embryos at different stages of development. Similar experiments with RNAs labeled at other stages and tested at different RNA/DNA ratios (Glisin et al., 1966; Hynes and Gross, 1972) confirmed this conclusion. The experiments of Glisin et al. (1966) also demonstrated cessation in the synthesis of some RNA. Amphibian (Denis, 1966) and fish (Kafiani, 1970) development is also characterized by a complex pattern of changes in multiple-copy transcripts. We now know that the reactions measured in our studies involve only the transcripts of repeated DNA sequences (up to C_0t 100; Britten and Kohne, 1968) whereas mRNA is apparently produced largely from nonrepeated sequences (Goldberg et al., 1973).

Although a systematic study of stage-specific transcription of unique genes has not been reported, the patterns of protein synthesized as development proceeds are clearly different (Gross, 1967; Mackintosh and Bell, 1969); these changes would probably arise by differential transcription of unique genes. Eckberg and Ozaki (1973) have reported that unique DNA sequences are represented in unfertilized egg RNA and increasingly in mid-blastulae and prisms. If reiterated sequences are transcribed concurrently or sequentially with unique segments of the genome, then changes in the former would indicate changes in unique transcripts. Our studies show that each major stage of development in the sand dollar has a characteristic complement of reiterated sequence transcripts—i.e., stage-specific RNAs—and that changes in the populations of these molecules are associated with the degree of differentiation. This is illustrated in Figs. 2 and 5. It is also evident that sequences similar to egg RNA are transcribed by all stages. Whether the egg-type RNAs being transcribed at each stage are qualitatively similar is not indicated, but a consideration, which will be made in a later section, of evolutionary conservatism of early and late egg-type RNAs suggests that they are not.

There is a modest increase in proportion of stage-specific RNA species until hatching and then a larger increase in gastrulae and prisms. Judging from the plateau levels approached when RNAs from the latter two stages are added in increasing amounts (Fig. 5A), species being made in hatching blastulae are not completely represented in the later stages, presumably because they have been degraded. In the 6 to 8 hours between hatching and the start of gastrulation, there is an onset of synthesis of new RNA populations not represented in hatching blastulae. These few hours, in short, involve several significant changes in the repeated sequence transcription: an increase and decline in accumulation of egg-type RNAs, a loss of species characteristic of hatching blastulae and a switching on of synthesis of RNAs from a new set of sequences.

A variety of evidence favors the conclusion that the egg-type RNA produced during oogenesis and/or synthesized after fertilization, supports cleavage and early development. It seems likely that relatively few new genes would be transcribed during this interval, since few new differentiations appear then: cilia, septate desmosomes, a few enzymes including the hatching enzyme, and various transport carriers (Whiteley and Chambers, 1966; Epel, 1975). The stage-specific transcripts appearing between hatching and gastrulation become evident at the start of the period of most complex morphological and physiological changes in the embryo. The synthesis of enzymes and other proteins increases abruptly and extensively. Motility and morphogenetic movements are greatly increased. Primary mesenchyme and ectoderm differentiate, and soon specialized endoderm, skeletal elements, and mesoderm will form. Pigment cells and other differentiated cells appear in both ectoderm and endoderm. It would be expected that such changes would require the expression of different sets of unique DNA sequences, and the observations of Fig. 5 indicate that these are accompanied by sizable qualitative changes in transcription of reiterated sequences. Indeed, the rather abrupt switchover after hatching suggests that there is a substantial programming change a few hours prior to the actual differentiation.

F. Evolutionary Relatedness of Echinoderm DNAs and RNAs

On the basis of the experiments reviewed above, two types of transcripts of reiterated DNA were distinguished during echinoderm development: egg-type RNAs and stage-specific RNAs. What are the evolutionary relationships between the DNA sequences encoding these two types of RNAs? To what extent have these kinds of sequences diverged during the evolution of echinoderm species? To study these questions, we have compared repeated DNA sequences and populations of RNA molecules from eggs and prism larvae of five echinoderm species: three sea urchins of the same genus, an echinoid of a separate superorder, and an asteroid. The systematic relationships of these species, based on morphological and paleontological criteria (Moore, 1966), are shown below:

Class Echinoidea
    Subclass Euechinoidea
        Superorder Echinacea
           Order Echinoida
                Family Strongylocentrotidae
                    Strongylocentrotus purpuratus (Stimpson)
                    Strongylocentrotus droebachiensis (O. F. Müller)
                    Strongylocentrotus franciscanus (A. Agassiz)
        Superorder Gnathostomata
           Order Clypeasteroida
                Family Dendrasteridae
                    Dendraster excentricus (Eschscholtz)
Class Asteroidea
                Pisaster ochraceus (Brandt)

The extent to which the reiterated sequences of the genome of *S. purpuratus*, *S. droebachiensis*, *S. franciscanus*, *D. excentricus*, and *P. ochraceus* are related was estimated from the binding of unlabeled DNA from each species with labeled DNA from either *S. purpuratus* or *D. excentricus*. The values of the left half of Fig. 8A and B correlate, in

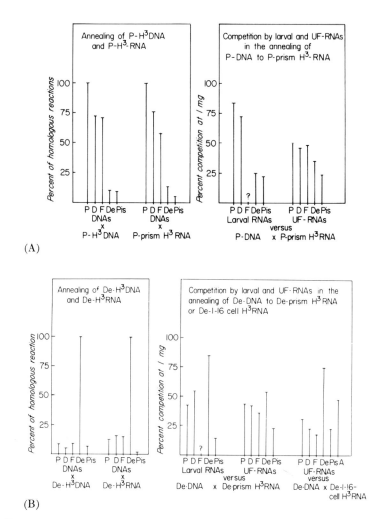

Fɪɢ. 8. Summary of extent of binding and competition reactions of DNAs and RNAs from *Strongylocentrotus purpuratus* (A) and *Dendraster excentricus* (B) to DNAs of five echinoderm species. Percent competition plotted for values obtained at 1 mg RNA per reaction mixture (2.9 mg RNA/ml). The following abbreviations are used: H³-RNA and DNA-³H-labeled RNA and DNA; P = *S. purpuratus;* D = *S. droebachiensis;* F = *S. franciscanus;* De = *D. excentricus;* Pis = *P. ochraceus;* A = *Allocentrotus fragilis;* ? = not measured. Data taken from Whiteley *et al.* (1970) and Mizuno *et al.* (1973).

general, with the systematic positions of the five species. All the DNA–DNA duplexes showed comparable levels of thermal stability and dissociated over a comparable range of temperatures (Whiteley *et al.,*

1970). Relative to homologous pairs, the ΔT_ms for hybrid duplexes formed with *S. purpuratus* DNA were: 0°C for *purpuratus–droebachiensis*, 2°C for *purpuratus–franciscanus*, 3°C for *purpuratus–excentricus*, and 4°C for *purpuratus–ochraceus*. These ΔT_m values correspond to 0–2.5% base-sequence divergence (Ullman and McCarthy, 1973) in this portion of the genome among the five species examined. Thus, the fidelity of base pairing for heterologous duplexes was reasonably good.

The DNA homology differences observed among the three strongylo-centrotids correspond to differences exhibited among mammals at the *ordinal* level (Hoyer *et al.*, 1964) and therefore, the extent of annealing between the reiterated DNA sequences of the more distant pairs of echinoderms examined is surprisingly high. The genus *Strongylocentrotus* is old relative to many modern mammalian genera, the earliest fossils being 30–50 million years old (Moore, 1966), a time sufficient to encompass the emergence of families or even orders of mammals; the two superorders (Gnathostomata and Echinacea) have been separated for about 200 million years, and the classes (Asteroidea and Echinoidea) for more than 600 million years. Therefore, the cross-reaction among the reiterated sequences of DNAs of higher echinoderm taxa indicates an extreme conservatism of some of the DNA sequences.

A similar assessment of the relatedness of RNAs transcribed from reiterated sequences is summarized also in the left half of Fig. 8A and B. In general, the extent of annealing of the newly synthesized prism RNAs parallels that found for DNA–DNA binding. Most of the transcripts of reiterated DNA synthesized at the late larval stages are, therefore, species-specific as well as stage-specific. A second question is whether the RNA populations *present* in the prism larvae of the five echinoderm species show similar interrelationships. This point was examined by determining the ability of unlabeled prism RNA of the various species to serve as a competitor in the binding of a selected prism RNA to its homologous DNA. The results of these experiments (including in the right half of Fig. 8A and 8B) demonstrate that RNA populations present in prisms are similar to those that are newly synthesized at this stage. Thus, with reference both to the relatedness of RNAs undergoing transcription in the prisms and the relatedness of RNAs accumulated in the larvae, these echinoderms fall into three groups—*purpuratus–droebachiensis–franciscanus, excentricus*, and *ochraceus*—which, of course, relate to the phylogenetic taxa.

The same approach was used to examine the homologies among the RNA populations present in the unfertilized eggs. Competition experiments were performed with RNAs from unfertilized eggs from all five species using ^{3}H-labeled RNA from prism stages of *S. purpuratus, S.*

droebaciensis, and *D. excentricus* as reference RNAs. We found that RNAs from unfertilized eggs of each species possess transcripts that compete effectively with the binding of each of the labeled prism RNAs to its homologous DNA. These competitions were considerably greater than expected on the basis of the relatedness of the species as determined by DNA–DNA annealing or from the relatedness of prism RNAs. Figure 8 indicates that the competing populations of RNA molecules in unfertilized eggs are more alike than are the total reiterated genomes. In the more distant pairings, the RNAs from the eggs compete more extensively than those from their larvae. Data using *S. droebachiensis* reference RNA confirm these statements, and the same conclusions are drawn from the nearly identical data (Whiteley *et al.*, 1970) obtained when the experiments are performed by sequential annealing. Further, we found that mixtures of RNAs ("additivity experiments") from unfertilized eggs of *S. purpuratus* and *D. excentricus* gave the same results as each RNA preparation tested alone suggesting that the same populations of competing molecules were involved in the two species. It is clear that egg-type RNA detected in larvae contains evolutionarily conservative sequences and that these are present in high frequency since the experiments were performed at low RNA/DNA ratios. Far more difference was apparent among the RNAs from unfertilized eggs when they were tested at high RNA/DNA ratios where differences are emphasized among species of RNA molecules present at low frequency.

Egg-type RNA populations synthesized *early* in development do not show the same degree of conservatism. When ^{3}H-labeled 1–16-cell RNA from *D. excentricus* was used as the reference, RNAs from unfertilized eggs of several species gave significantly less competition (Fig. 8B) than was found in experiments utilizing reference RNA from prisms. Apparently, the egg-type RNA synthesized early in development is enriched in species-specific RNA populations and, thus, represents a different subset of the transcripts characterizing the egg than those synthesized at the prism stage. For example, it may be speculated that histone mRNAs constitute a greater proportion of egg RNA during early cleavage than in late larval development. Histone mRNAs have been shown to be relatively species specific in echinoderms (Weinberg *et al.*, 1972); the degree of competition would then be affected by the relative amount of this multiple-copy RNA in the total population whose reaction is being measured. The conservative egg-type RNAs may predominate in the larval subset because they may be related to processes or syntheses characteristic of that stage which have remained little changed in evolution, such as the synthesis of the basic proteins of ribosomes, which appear to be very similar among classes of echinoderms (Strathman, 1967). Whatever their function, the conservative egg-type sequences could hardly have remained in the genome for this great length of time without random drift if they did not confer important adaptive advantages to the organisms possessing them.

G. GENE EXPRESSION IN BLOCKED ECHINOID HYBRIDS

The systematic relationships, as well as the extent of DNA homology among the reiterated portions of the genomes of several echinoderm species discussed in the preceding section, would predict that partially successful hybridization could occur between at least some of the species. Such hybrids can, in fact, be produced and have been intensively investigated, starting with the initial studies of Baltzer (1910), Tennent (1912, 1922), and Moore (1913). Aside from being objects of interest in their own right, these hybrids offer a system for potential analysis of questions of more general interest. With regard to evolutionary relationships, do interspecies combinations express primarily their conserved, shared genes, or their species-specific genes, or is there a normal balance in this respect? Other questions pertain to the analysis of interaction of nuclear and cytoplasmic factors in the production, processing, and expression of genetic information in cells. These hybrids, like somatic cell hybrids, have broad sets of markers, which are recognizable in the genome and at the transcriptional and translational levels. Last, when a major developmental event in a hybrid combination shows a particular lesion, such as blockage at gastrulation, can the hybrid be used to help us understand the regulation of this event in normal development?

We have investigated the hybrid *D. excentricus* ♀ × *S. purpuratus* ♂, which blocks at gastrulation. As shown in the preceding section, although these species are only distantly related, they possess evolutionarily conservative segments in the reiterated portions of their genomes and large portions which are species specific. The purpose of our studies was to determine whether both parental genomes are faithfully replicated, transcribed, and translated in the hybrid produced by this superordinal cross.

The rates of development of the two parental species are quite different, so that *D. excentricus* (abbreviated DeDe), at 15°, reaches the late prism stage (Fig. 9A) in 34 hours whereas *S. purpuratus* (PP) reaches the same stage in 53 hours. The hybrid larva, *D. excentricus* ♀ × *S. purpuratus* ♂, designated DeP, develops normally up to gastrulation and is then severely retarded and blocks in the condition shown in Fig. 9B. It remains alive and without apparent necrosis for many hours. Details of morphology and cytology of the hybrid are given elsewhere (Whiteley and Whiteley, 1972).

The varied kinds of hybrids resulting from echinoid crosses can be

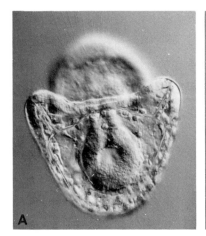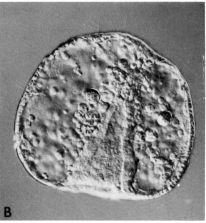

FIG. 9. Normal *Dendraster excentricus* embryos cultured for 54 hours at 12°C (A) and blocked *D. excentricus* × *Strongylocentrotus purpuratus* hybrid embryos of the same age (B). Photographed with Nomarski optics. From Whiteley and Whiteley (1972).

classified (Tennent, 1922) as: (a) true hybrids in which all chromosomes are retained, (b) partial hybrids with some elimination of paternal chromosomes, and (c) false hybrids in which only maternal chromosomes are retained. Both true and false hybrids may produce viable embryos, and both types also can be blocked and produce nonviable larval stages. In DeP, the sperm nucleus can observed (Nomarski optics) to enter the egg and to fuse with the egg pronucleus. A test of the presence of paternal DNA in the resulting embryos was made by annealing ³H-labeled RNA synthesized by the DeP larva to normal DNA from both sand dollar and sea urchin sperm. The average of several experiments showed that 56.4% of the radioactivity binding to DNA reacted with De-DNA and the proportion binding to P-DNA was 43.6%, a ratio of 1.29. Since the genome of De is 1.22 times larger than that of P, it may be concluded that the reiterated portions of both parental genomes are replicated, about equally, in the hybrid. In this respect, this superordinal combination is different from the *Paracentrotus–Arbacia* hybrid, which Denis and Brachet (1969) have found to be aneuploid, deficient particularly in paternal DNA.

Studies of the thermal dissociation of the DNA–DNA duplexes made by annealing De-DNA or P-DNA to ³H-labeled DeP DNA gave identical melting curves with T_m values of 72–72.5°C. The homologous DNA duplexes (DeDe and PP), produced under the same conditions of annealing, also had T_m values of 72°C whereas native DNA of each species had a

T_m of 82°C. Thus, each parental DNA synthesized by the hybrid had the same fidelity of base pairing as DNA extracted from normal DeDe and PP embryos.

A few experiments with labeled RNA extracted under identical conditions from parallel cultures of DeDe larvae and DeP larvae showed that the two preparations had very similar specific activities suggesting that both larvae synthesized RNA with an equal efficiency. Radioautography of the labeled DeDe and DeP larvae demonstrated the same cytological pattern of incorporation in both: intensive synthesis of RNA in ectoderm, somewhat less in endoderm, and still less in mesenchyme.

Annealing experiments using ³H-labeled RNA extracted from DeP larvae (Fig. 10) provided evidence that approximately equal transcrip-

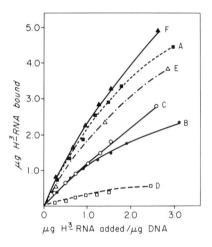

FIG. 10. Annealing of ³H-labeled RNA (H³-RNA) from prisms of *Dendraster excentricus* (DeDe) and blocked gastrulae of *D. excentricus* ♀ × *Strongylocentrotus purpuratus* ♂ (DeP) to P-DNA and De-DNA. A = binding of ³H-DeDe RNA to De-DNA; B = binding of ³H-DeP RNA to De-DNA; C = binding of ³H-DeP RNA to P-DNA; D = binding of ³H-DeDe RNA to P-DNA; E = binding of ³H-DeP RNA to equal amounts of P-DNA and De-DNA added together to the reaction mixtures; F = sum of curves B and D. The two labeled reference RNAs used in these experiments had equal specific activities. From Whiteley and Whiteley (1972).

tion of the reiterated segments of each parental genome occurred (curves B and C) and that the annealing to the paternal (P) DNA greatly exceeded that attributable to the relatedness of the two species (curves A and D). Duplexes formed by annealing hybrid ³H-labeled RNA to paternal and maternal DNA had the same thermal stability as homologous duplexes (i.e., those produced by annealing DeDe-RNA to De-DNA and by annealing PP-RNA to P-DNA). In the *Paracentrotus–Arbacia* hybrid, however, RNA synthesis was predominantly paternal even though there was considerable loss of the paternal genome (Denis and Brachet, 1969). Competition experiments disclosed that normal embryos of both the maternal and paternal type produce stage-specific transcripts as well as populations which are synthesized throughout development. Transcription of the maternal genome by the *Paracentrotus–Arbacia* hybrid yielded both kinds of molecules; transcription of the paternal genome produced only the populations of molecules normally synthesized throughout development (Denis and Brachet, 1970). Thus, the *Paracentrotus–Arbacia* hybrid differs from the DeP hybrid both in replication and in patterns of transcription.

We have used RNA from unfertilized eggs to detect the presence of the evolutionarily conservative egg-type species in the RNA from DeP larvae and have used prism RNAs to detect stage-specific, species-specific populations. Thus, in these experiments reference (pulse-labeled) RNA from DeP embryos was titrated to determine whether both De-DNA and P-DNA sequences were represented. An example of these experiments is given in Fig. 11, derived from full competition curves previously pub-

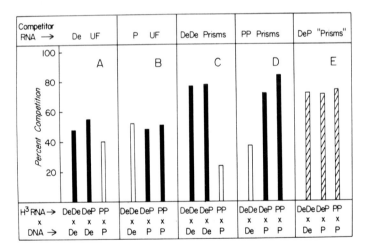

Fig. 11. Summary of competition experiments comparing the effects of unfertilized egg (UF) RNAs and prism RNAs on the binding of ³H-labeled RNA (H³-RNA) from *Dendraster excentricus* (DeDe), *Strongylocentrotus purpuratus* (PP), and hybrid *D. excentricus* ♀ × *S. purpuratus* ♂ (DeP) embryos. Percent competition obtained at 1 mg RNA per reaction mixture (2.9 mg/ml) in experiments using RNA from: unfertilized eggs of *D. excentricus* (A); unfertilized eggs of *S. purpuratus* (B); prisms of *D. excentricus* (C); prisms of *S. purpuratus* (D); and blocked DeP hybrids (E). Each competitor was tested in the binding of ³H-labeled RNAs to DNA as indicated at the bottom of the figure. Data taken from Whiteley and Whiteley (1972).

lished (Whiteley and Whiteley, 1972; Whiteley et al., 1970). In panels A and B the egg-type sequences are tested. In panel A are results of allowing the hybrid reference RNA to react with maternal DNA in the presence of competing RNA from unfertilized sand dollar eggs. In B, the representation of egg-type paternal sequences is shown. Panels C and D similarly show the representation in the hybrid reference RNA of maternal (C) and paternal (D) sequences which characterize normal advanced prism larvae. The combination under test in each panel is accented, and each panel includes the corresponding homologous reaction for comparison. An examination of these data will show that the sequences complementary to maternal and paternal genomes contain both conservative egg-type and larval species-specific members. Further, these are present in the typical proportions inasmuch as the annealings to both DNAs are competed by the normal RNAs essentially as in homologous reactions. These data, together with those in panel E, show that the hybrid larvae, despite being developmentally blocked, have produced and accumulated transcripts from both genomes to the same extent as in normal maternal and paternal prism larvae.

Neyfakh, Kafiani, and their associates (Kafiani, 1970; Neyfakh, 1971) have studied quantitative aspects of RNA synthesis in a loach $\times$ goldfish hybrid and in an androgenetic haploid hybrid (loach cytoplasm $\times$ goldfish nucleus) and concluded that each chromosome set is triggered to synthesize RNA at the normal time by the cytoplasm and that each set is transcribed at the normal rate. The androgenetic haploid hybrids block as blastulae, however, and they concluded that in these embryos, as we have found also in the echinoid hybrid, both kinds of nuclei seem to function, but without developmental success.

Our studies on the replication and transcription of the repeated sequences in the blocked hybrid suggested the possibility that the paternal genome was not only replicated and transcribed, but also expressed at the level of protein synthesis. In other hybrids, deficiencies have been detected in the synthesis of paternal proteins: e.g., Badman and Brookbank (1972) reported that the reciprocal hybrid (PDe) does not produce detectable paternal antigens, and Neyfakh and his associates (Neyfakh, 1971) have found quantitative deficiencies in translation of paternal RNAs in a loach–goldfish androgenetic haploid hybrid.

An examination was made of esterases (Ozaki, 1965, 1975) in four blocked echinoid hybrids (DeP, PDe, D. excentricus ♀ × S. drobachiensis ♂, and S. droebachiensis ♀ × D. excentricus ♂) and malate dehydrogenases in DeP (Ozaki and Whiteley, 1970) using differences in electrophoretic mobility to distinguish between maternal and paternal forms of the enzymes. In these experiments, only the maternal form of each

enzyme could be detected. DeP embryos also fail to synthesize echino-
chromes, which may reflect inability to make one or more key enzymes.

We have tested the parentage of the hatching enzyme synthesized by
the DeP hybrid. To do this, small numbers of cleavage or early blastula
stage sea urchin and sand dollar embryos were added to a culture of
hybrid larvae which had been concentrated to an approximately 25%
suspension just prior to hatching. When the hybrids hatched, the hatching
enzyme released into the sea water attacked the fertilization membranes
of the test embryos. Only the sand dollar test embryos were denuded
by the enzyme, as is shown in Fig. 12. Control experiments of the same
design showed that PP and DeDe hatching blastulae secreted species-
specific enzyme. Hatching of normal sea urchin and sand dollar embryos
was greatly retarded by cultivation from first cleavage in the presence

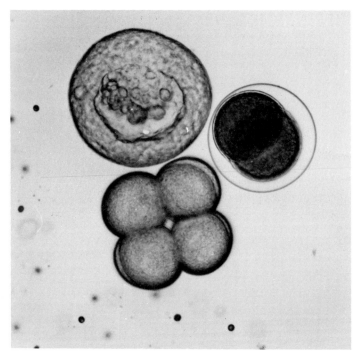

Fig. 12. Specificity of the hatching enzyme produced by *Dendraster excentricus*
♀ × *Strongylocentrotus purpuratus* ♂ (DeP) larvae. DeP larvae were concentrated
just prior to hatching, and normal fertilized eggs of *D. excentricus* and *S. purpuratus*
were added to the culture during the time of hatching of the hybrids. The smaller
2-cell stage embryo with an intact fertilization membrane is *S. purpuratus;* the 4-cell
embryo without a fertilization membrane is *D. excentricus;* the early mesenchyme
blastula is a DeP hybrid.

of 20 μg of actinomycin D per milliliter and was entirely blocked by 30 μg/ml. The latter concentration, tested at the normal hatching time, reduced incorporation of uridine-^{3}H (60-minute interval) in sea urchin and sand dollar embryos by 60% and 55%, respectively, whereas incorporation of valine-^{14}C (10-minute interval) was not affected. Also, 5 μg of cordycepin (3'-deoxyadenosine) per milliliter greatly delayed hatching of *S. purpuratus*, and 10 μg/ml completely blocked it. These preliminary experiments with cordycepin have been confirmed by J. Spieth (personal communication) and extended to *D. excentricus*. Together, these observations indicate that newly synthesized and, presumably, adenylylated mRNA is needed for hatching. It follows, therefore, that the hybrid secretes hatching enzyme primarily of maternal parentage derived from newly made RNA.

However, an investigation of the histones synthesized by DeP embryos disclosed that at least one paternal protein, the F1 histone, is produced in the hybrid (Easton *et al.*, 1974). An electrophoretic analysis (Fig. 13A) of histones extracted from the chromatin of DeDe and PP

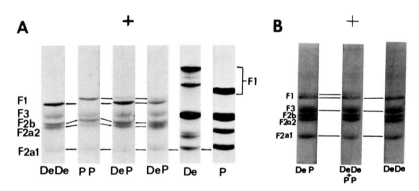

FIG. 13. An electrophoretic comparison of the histones from *Dendraster excentricus* (DeDe), *Strongylocentrotus purpuratus* (PP), and *D. excentricus* ♀ × *S. purpuratus* ♂ (DeP). (A) Histones were extracted from hatched blastulae of DeDe and PP and hatched blastulae and blocked gastrulae of DeP and electrophoresed as described by Easton *et al.* (1974). Histones from sperm of both parental species (De and P) are shown for comparison. (B) Comparison of DeP histones with the pattern obtained by coelectrophoresis of a mixture of DeDe and PP histones. From Easton *et al.* (1974).

embryos revealed three differences in gel electrophoresis patterns: the F1, F2b, and F2a2 histones of normal DeDe blastulae migrated more rapidly than the corresponding PP histones. Histones extracted from the DeP hybrid (either from hatched blastulae or from the blocked gastrula stage) contained F1 species characteristic of both parents, but it has not been possible to resolve the F2b and F2a2 bands. A control experiment (Fig. 13B) demonstrated that two F1 bands, corresponding to the two parental bands, can be detected when mixtures of histones from the two parents are coelectrophoresed.

An additional hybrid (DDe) was made by fertilizing eggs of *S. droebachiensis* (D) with sperm of *D. excentricus* (De) ; with these species, the reciprocal cross (DeD) is also easily made. Figure 14 shows

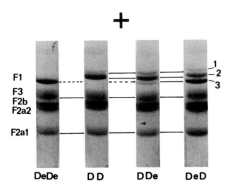

FIG. 14. An electrophoretic comparison of histones from *Dendraster excentricus* (DeDe), *Strongylocentrotus droebachiensis* (DD) and the hybrids DDe, and DeD) between them. Histones were extracted from hatched blastula stages of both parental types and the two hybrids. From Easton *et al.* (1974).

that the normal DD embryos have two components in the F1 histone band in place of the single F1 band seen in DeDe embryos. In both DDe and DeD, both F1 histone components were detected. In all three of these hybrids, smaller amounts (18–31%) of the paternal specific F1 histone were produced, judging from scans of stained gels. The difference in proportion of paternal and maternal F1 histone doubtless reflects the fact that the maternal forms are translated from both stored egg and newly transcribed larval messages, whereas the paternal forms can be translated only from new messages. Thus, it is apparent that there is a limited expression of the paternal genome at the level of protein synthesis. Of the small sample of specific proteins studied in these hybrids, only the histones are known to be encoded in reiterated sequences. Their synthesis and the absence of the others may suggest that functioning of reiterated, but not unique, sequences is normal in these hybrids. Potentially such a dichotomy could be at the level of transcription, but it could also reflect specific controls in subsequent steps. Another distinction between histone and other messages, which may be relevant, is that only the former are polyadenylylated. We have not been able to resolve whether small amounts of all paternal histones are produced or whether only the F1 histone is made. It should be noted, in this connection, that cistrons coding for the F1 histones are not clustered with the other four histone genes (Birnstiel et al., 1974), and this may be related to the expression of the paternal form of this histone message by the hybrids.

Last, we have employed an immunological analysis to determine the extent of synthesis of a broad spectrum of paternal proteins derived, we assume, from single-copy messages (J. P. Chamberlain, A. H. Whiteley, and H. R. Whiteley, unpublished observations). In these experiments, DeP embryos and normal DeDe and PP embryos were cultivated to early gastrula stage (i.e., before the block to development of DeP has been well established) and incubated for 70 minutes with a mixture of 15 ^{3}H-labeled amino acids. The labeled proteins were then extracted. Parallel DeDe and PP cultures were cultivated to the same stage and extracted in the same way, but without exposure to the labeled amino acids; rabbits were immunized with aliquots of the latter preparations. The antisera were then used in radioimmune precipitation studies designed to detect the presence of S. purpuratus antigens in DeP hybrids.

Figure 15A shows that proteins present in the extract of ^{3}H-labeled DeDe embryos were precipitated by De-antiserum and that there was a very sizable cross-reaction when the same antiserum was tested with the ^{3}H-labeled proteins extracted from normal PP embryos. The reciprocal experiments with PP proteins and P-antiserum gave similar results (Fig. 15B). The immunological cross-reactions are of particular interest in view of the interrelatedness of the reiterated nucleic acids discussed earlier (Fig. 8). It is probable that the antigens are largely encoded by the unique part of the genome. The immunological cross-reactions with the solubilized antigens are about 30%, which exceeds the 10–13% relatedness indicated by the hybridization experiments with reiterated DNAs and the RNAs derived from them. This suggests either that relatedness of unique sequences will be found to exceed that of reiterated ones or that these larval events have involved expression of a preponderance of the conservative genomes.

The data obtained with ^{3}H-labeled DeP proteins (Fig. 15C) show that most of the antigens synthesized at the onset of the block were maternal—in fact, the amount of labeled precipitate detected with each antiserum could not be distinguished from the reactions observed in the experiments of Fig. 15A. The substantial cross-reactions were almost entirely eliminated when the antisera were absorbed by the heterologous antigens (Fig. 15D and E), demonstrating that the cross-reactions derived from expression of conservative sequences. The absorbed anti-De antiserum reacted as effectively with labeled hybrid as with labeled sand dollar antigens (Fig. 15F) from which it is concluded that the hybrids synthesize an undiminished proportion of the soluble maternal antigens.

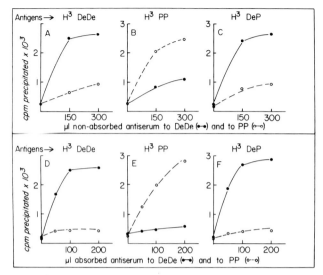

Fig. 15. Detection of De-specific and P-specific antigens by radioimmune assay. (A, B, and C). Radioactivity of ³H-labeled (H³) antigens from *Dendraster excentricus* (DeDe), *Strongylocentrotus purpuratus* (PP), and hybrid (DeP) precipitated by non-absorbed antiserum to DeDe and PP. (D, E, and F). Radioactivity of ³H-labeled DeDe, PP, and DeP precipitated by absorbed antiserum to DeDe and PP.

Embryos, labeled as described in the text, were suspended after washing, in 0.5 M NaCl–0.01 M Tris buffer, pH 8.0, homogenized, and centrifuged at 10,000 rpm for 10 minutes to remove large particulates; the supernatant fractions (labeled antigens) containing 10 μg of protein per milliliter and having specific activities (cpm/μg protein) of 14,373 for DeDe, 22,491 for PP, and 17,962 for DeP were retained. Fifty microliters of labeled antigen were mixed with various amounts of antiserum in a total volume of 250 μl, left at room temperature for 1 hour and in an ice bath for 2–3 hours, diluted with 3 ml of 0.1 M NaCl–0.01 M Tris buffer, pH 8.0 and centrifuged at 3000 rpm. The precipitates were resuspended in the same buffer, recentrifuged, and dissolved in 10% NCS, and the radioactivity was determined. Addition of 0.05–0.25 ml of control sera (nonabsorbed, preimmunization) to any of the ³H-labeled antigens resulted in the precipitation of 100–150 cpm. Absorbed sera were prepared as described above using 0.25 ml of ³H-labeled antigens from DeDe or PP and 1.0 ml of each antiserum.

However, there is no clearly positive reaction with the absorbed anti-P antiserum.

A more sensitive assay, based on the ability of the unlabeled homologous proteins to compete in the antigen–antibody reaction, revealed that DeP extracts do contain a small amount of P antigen. As shown in Fig. 16, the interaction of absorbed P-antiserum with ³H-labeled P proteins was decreased progressively in the presence of increasing amounts of unlabeled P-proteins; De-proteins did not interfere in this reaction. However, addition of DeP extract caused a slight but reproducible decrease

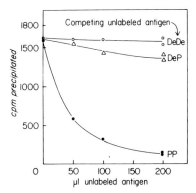

FIG. 16. The effect of unlabeled antigen preparation on the P-specific antigen–antibody radioimmune precipitation. Fifty microliters of ³H-labeled *Strongylocentrotus purpuratus* (PP) antigen were mixed with 100 μl of antiserum to PP which had been absorbed with DeDe antigen, and various amounts of unlabeled antigens were added as indicated in a total volume of 250 μl. The radioactivity of the precipitated antigen–antibody complex was determined as described for Fig. 15.

in the P-specific antigen-antibody reaction. These data indicate, therefore, that although a small amount of the *paternal* genetic information is translated into immunologically detectable components, certainly most of the soluble amino-acid labeled antigens synthesized by DeP at the time of the block are maternal.

Overall, these studies indicate that replication of the reiterated parts of both parental genomes in DeP is normal even though the two species are very distantly related. Their transcription is also normal and at least some of the multiple copy transcripts are used and expressed as shown by the histone studies. The block to development may arise from defects in replication or transcription of the unique part of the genome, which we have not yet examined directly. We infer from the immunological reactions that the unique sequences of De must be present and expressed in the hybrid. We have no positive evidence concerning the unique sequences of P, except for the small P-specific immunological reaction noted. Conceivably, the entire paternal genome could be replicated normally and be transcribed to produce normal primary gene products—the polymerases may function indiscriminately using both genomes. However, one or more of the events of packaging, processing, and transport of the heterogeneous RNAs may require species-specific proteins which could not be produced in this self-limiting system. A similar argument may apply to the events of translation. If any of the initiation, translocation, or termination factors are specific, the *Dendraster* cytoplasm would be unable to translate the *S. purpuratus* mRNAs. The possibility could equally well exist that there are P-specific restrictive or repressive proteins as well as those having a positive function. In the instance of somatic cell hybrids in which translation of both genomes has been observed, the evolutionary disparity between the involved species is much less than between the two echinoderms and the processing or translational factors might still cross-react. Last, defects in morphogenesis could arise from a mistiming in the expression of the paternal genomes or because of asynchrony in development due to the expression of each genome on its own intrinsic schedule.

IV. Summary Statement

The following points have been made concerning the transcripts of reiterated DNA in echinoid eggs and embryos: the egg RNA is cytoplasmic, carried in particles roughly 30 S in size; it includes both polyadenylylated and nonadenylylated molecules and encodes many peptides, including histones, tubulin, and ribonucleotide reductase. Egg RNA contains repeated DNA transcripts. It is not known whether these are part of all egg RNAs or are on certain classes, nor if they are congruent with encoding RNA. Based on melting characteristics and size heterogeneity, it is probable that the multiple-copy species include histone mRNA as well as other transcripts. There is essentially no RNA synthesis prior to fertilization, but synthesis of egg RNA is renewed after fertilization and accelerates after the 64-cell stage. During cleavage, there is a substantial augmentation of egg-type RNA, with a decline after hatching. Some of these transcripts are made at all stages through the prism stage. There is no specific segregation of these RNAs among blastomeres, but at the 16-cell stage, micromeres are activated to begin the first detectable cell-specific transcription. Additional stage-specific transcription occurs during late cleavage but hatching signals a substantial increase, correlated with increased synthesis of new species of proteins and with morphogenesis. At the same time, there is probably both a quantitative and a qualitative decline in the production of egg-type RNAs with a continued synthesis of those which are evolutionarily the most conservative. The stage-specific transcripts are largely species-specific whereas egg-type ones are less so. Those made in late larvae are especially conservative while those produced in early cleavage include a subset which is more species-specific.

The sand dollar-sea urchin hybrid replicates both genomes and transcribes them with equal efficiency. The pattern of transcription of the reiterated segments is normal for both genomes until well after an irreversible block in morphogenesis has set in, both with regard to egg-type and stage-specific sequences. A number of specific proteins are produced only from the maternal genome and only a very small percentage of the total soluble antigens synthesized prior to the block is paternal in origin. Therefore, there is a gap between transcription of reiterated sequences and translation of mRNAs encoded in the paternal genome. The notable exception is the F1 histone, which is made very early and probably throughout development, and is produced in both the maternal and paternal forms.

Overall, these patterns of changes in the transcripts of reiterated DNA sequences are consistent with developmental events and are not inconsistent with the various models of transcriptional regulation mentioned earlier. We wish, finally, to examine the changes chronicled above in the light of one of the models in which the roles of repeated DNA are clearly defined, although other models are not specifically excluded.

The model described by Georgiev et al. (1974); Georgiev (1969, 1972) proposed that a transcriptional unit consists of a promoter site to which polymerase can attach, an acceptor zone and a structural gene located near the 3′ end. The acceptor zone is viewed as being a large segment consisting of many sites capable of binding regulatory proteins; many of these sites may be repeated within one transcriptional unit or may be shared among different transcriptional units. Therefore, if two different sets of units are transcribed, two different populations of reiterated DNA transcripts will be produced in the nucleus concomitant with two populations of messages. The model proposes that the most frequently shared acceptor sites are closest to the promoter end of the unit. Thus, families of multiple copy sequences with different reiteration frequencies are produced from the transcription of many units. The structural zone, located distal to the acceptor zone toward the 3′ end, includes a starting signal (possibly an internal repeat), a nonreiterated informational segment coding for a structural gene and a terminus. Heterogeneous nuclear RNA is produced by transcription of the entire unit. Transcription of entire units is regulated at least in part by interaction with histones, especially by modification or removal of F1 histone. Additional regulation occurs at the level of packaging and processing of heterogeneous nuclear RNA; the former process involves specific interactions with informofers and the second involves degradation of the noninformational RNA by end-and exonucleases.

In terms of this model, the virtual absence of RNA synthesis in unfertilized echinoid eggs could arise by blockage of the promoter site or by interaction of a regulatory protein with an acceptor site immediately adjacent to the promoter; the progressively increasing rate of transcription following fertilization would mean a progressive availability of these sites to polymerase following removal of the block rather than increases in the amounts of the RNA polymerases. Possibly, removal of the block could involve F1 histones. It is known that the F1 histones of sea urchin gametes and embryos are qualitatively different (Ozaki, 1971; Easton and Chalkley, 1972) and that changes in histone patterns are correlated with the template capacity of chromatin (sperm chromatin is virtually inactive as a template for RNA polymerase whereas chromatin derived from embryos is active; Ozaki, 1971). The factors responsible for the concomitant and perhaps coordinate activation of transcription of the mitochondrial and nuclear genomes are not explained by the model.

Our data suggest that a small, relatively constant, set of units is transcribed during cleavage producing increasing numbers of simple and constant sets of multiple-copy transcripts and, we suppose, their regulated messages. The renewed synthesis of egg RNA after fertilization and continuation after cleavage could occur if the sets of acceptor sites transcribed during oogenesis remained unblocked in the unfertilized eggs—i.e., if RNA synthesis in the unfertilized egg were regulated by blockage at or immediately adjacent to the promoter sites. Then, removal of the latter block would restart the transcriptional program characteristic of oogenesis. It is not known whether the cytoplasmically located RNA molecules which we have measured in unfertilized eggs are also those molecules which code for histones, tubulin, and other polypeptides encoded in egg RNA. If so, they would appear to represent versions of heterogeneous nuclear RNA transported to the cytoplasm and the explanation for the retention of the segment transcribed from the reiterated acceptor may relate to the long-term cytoplasmic storage of the informational part of the molecules.

Cell-specific transcription, as in the micromeres, and stage-specific transcription initiated at hatching, may be explained as the consequence of unblocking of additional acceptor sites and/or by activation of new promoter sites. If different sets of genes shared common promoter sites (an aspect which is not necessarily part of Georgiev's model), a mechanism for the coordinated initiation of a number of sets of functionally related (e.g., stage-specific) genes would exist. These events would provide for the production of sets of new reiterated DNA transcripts such as those described above and, we suppose, for the unique transcripts which they regulate.

Georgiev's model provides no explanation for our finding that some reiterated DNA transcripts are more conservative than others in evolutionary terms. It is possible that transcriptional units with longer acceptor zones may have undergone more mutational and recombinational events leading to greater base sequence diversification whereas those with shorter acceptor zones may have retained sites with less divergence. If this is indeed the case, the more conservative DNA transcripts would be present on shorter heterogeneous nuclear RNA molecules. The model was not developed expressly for cistrons such as rRNA or histones, where the structural genes are arranged as numerous tandem repeats. The processed parts of the precursors for these cistrons are relatively smaller than in the transcriptional units of the model and, in line with the above argument, the structural parts are conservative. Possibly, a more conserved acceptor zone would regulate a conserved structural zone, but evidence for such a relationship does not exist other than in the correlation between conservatism of multiple copy transcripts in echinoderms and the immunological cross-reactivity between sand dollar and sea urchin described in an earlier section.

The hybrids represent an unusual situation and one that may help to establish the validity of aspects of the above model. The multiple copy segments of RNA representing both species are present in extracts of whole embryos but the paternal informational sequences are either absent or masked. If they are absent, then the paternal acceptor zone has been copied to the neighborhood of the structural zone and then the transcription has been terminated. Alternatively, the informational (3′) end of the heterogeneous molecule has been degraded back to the reiterated stretches. The existence of complete maternal heterogeneous nuclear RNAs in the hybrid and paternal ones lacking the structural segment as predicted by these observations is open to examination. An alternative explanation for the hybrid situation involves packaging of the primary transcript with its informofers and its processing by nucleases to mRNA. It is not yet known whether the lack of translation of the paternal genome may be due to the absence of appropriate informofers for the paternal transcripts or to defects in other steps between the production of the large primary transcript and the utilization of its informational segment in translation. It is of interest, and is probably significant, that the F1 histone is successfully synthesized in these larvae, which may correlate with the transcription of its message from a different kind of unit than that entailed in the model and the lack of adenylylation in its processing. The transcriptional units of Georgiev's model would account for the appearance of changing populations of multiple copy transcripts in heterogeneous nuclear RNA; the transcriptional units for tandem repeat elements would lead to the appearance of reiterated DNA transcripts in the cytoplasm.

ACKNOWLEDGMENTS

We acknowledge with pleasure the contributions of our colleagues to our published research. The unpublished research described here has included substantial contributions from Drs. John Chamberlain and Merrill Hille. We are particularly indebted to them and to Drs. Yang Rim Lee, Shigeki Mizuno, and Douglas Easton for helpful discussions. The research has been supported by grants from the American Cancer Society (VC-46B), the National Institute of Arthritis and Metabolic Diseases (Am-1311), and the National Science Foundation. HRW is the recipient of Research Career Award K6-GM-442 from the National Institutes of Heatlh.

REFERENCES

Aronson, A. I., and Wilt, F. H. (1969). *Proc. Nat. Acad. Sci. U.S.* **62**, 186.

Badman, W. S., and Brookbank, J. W. (1970). *Develop. Biol.* **21**, 243.

Baltzer, F. (1910). *Arch. Zellforsch.* **4**, 497.

Barrett, D., and Angelo, G. M. (1969). *Exp. Cell Res.* **57**, 159.

Beerman, W. (1972). *In* "Results and Problems—Cell Differentiation" (W. Beerman, J. Reinert, and H. Ursprung, eds.), Vol. 4, p. 1. Springer-Verlag, Berlin and New York.

Birnstiel, M., Telford, J., Weinberg, E., and Stafford, D. (1974). *Proc. Nat. Acad. Sci. U.S.* **71**, 2900.

Bonner, J., and Wu, J. R. (1973). *Proc. Nat. Acad. Sci. U.S.* **70**, 535.

Brandhorst, B. P., and Humphreys, T. (1971). *Biochemistry* **10**, 877.

Brandhorst, B. P., and Humphreys, T. (1972). *J. Cell Biol.* **53**, 474.

Britten, R. J., and Davidson, E. H. (1969). *Science* **165**, 349.

Britten, R. J., and Davidson, E. H. (1972). *Quart. Rev. Biol.* **46**, 111.

Britten, R. J., and Kohne, D. (1968). *Science* **161**, 529.

Britten, R. J., Graham, D. E., and Henerey, M. (1972). *Carnegie Inst. Wash., Yearb.* **71**, 270.

Brookbank, J. W., and Cummins, J. E. (1972). *Develop. Biol.* **29**, 234.

Chamberlain, J. P. (1970). *Biochim. Biophys. Acta* **213**, 183.

Chamberlain, J. P., and Metz, C. B. (1972). *J. Mol. Biol.* **64**, 593.

Church, R. B., and McCarthy, B. J. (1968). *Biochem. Genet.* **2**, 55.

Comb, D. G., Katz, S., Branda, P., and Pinzino, C. J. (1965). *J. Mol. Biol.* **14**, 195.

Craig, S. P. (1970). *J. Mol. Biol.* **47**, 615.

Craig, S. P., and Piatigorsky, J. (1971). *Develop. Biol.* **24**, 214.

Crippa, J., Davidson, E. H., and Mirsky, A. E. (1967). *Proc. Nat. Acad. Sci. U.S.* **67**, 885.

Crippa, M., Meza, I., and Dina, D. (1974). *Cold Spring Harbor Symp. Quant. Biol.* **38**, 933.

Czihak, G. (1965). *Wilhelm Roux' Arch. Entwicklungsmech. Organismen* **156**, 505.

Czihak, G., and Hörstadius, S. (1970). *Develop. Biol.* **22**, 15.

Daneholt, B., and Hosick, H. (1974). *Cold Spring Harbor Symp. Quant. Biol.* **38**, 629.

Darnell, J. E., Jelinek, W. R., and Molloy, G. R. (1973). *Science* **181**, 1215.

Davidson, E. H., and Britten, R. J. (1973). *Quart. Rev. Biol.* **48**, 565.

Davidson, E. H., and Hough, B. R. (1971). *J. Mol. Biol.* **56**, 491.

Davidson, E. H., Hough, B. R., Amenson, C. S., and Britten, R. J. (1973). *J. Mol. Biol.* **77**, 1.

Denis, H. (1966). *J. Mol. Biol.* **22**, 269 and 285.

Denis, H., and Brachet, J. (1969). *Proc. Nat. Acad. Sci. U.S.* **62**, 194 and 438.

Denis, H., and Brachet, J. (1970). *Eur. J. Biochem.* **13**, 86.

Denny, P. C., and Tyler, A. (1964). *Biochem. Biophys. Res. Commun.* **14**, 245.

DePetrocellis, B. (1974). Personal communication.

Dina, D., Crippa, M., and Beccari, E. (1973). *Nature (London), New Biol.* **242**, 101.

Dina, D., Meza, I., and Crippa, M. (1974). *Nature (London)*, **248**, 486.

Easton, D. P., and Chalkley, R. (1972). *Exp. Cell Res.* **72**, 502.

Easton, D. P., Chamberlain, J. P., Whiteley, A. H., and Whiteley, H. R. (1974). *Biochem. Biophys. Res. Commun.* **57**, 513.

Eckberg, W. R., and Ozaki, H. (1972). *Exp. Cell Res.* **73**, 177.

Eckberg, W. R., and Ozaki, H. (1973). *Amer. Soc. Zool.* **13**, 1316 (abstr.)

Eckhardt, R. A. (1972). *In* "Evolution of Genetic Systems" (H. H. Smith, ed.), p. 27. Gordon & Breach, New York.

Emerson, C. P., and Humphreys, T. (1970). *Develop. Biol.* **23**, 86.

Emerson, C. P., and Humphreys, T. (1971). *Science* **171**, 899.

Epel, D. (1967). *Proc. Nat. Acad. Sci. U.S.* **57**, 899.

Epel, D. (1975). *Amer. Zool.* **15**, (3).

Farquhar, M. N., and McCarthy, B. J. (1973). *Biochem. Biophys. Res. Commun.* **53**, 515.

Ficq, A., and Brachet, J. (1963). *Exp. Cell Res.* **32**, 90.

Flamm, W. G., Walker, P. M. B., and McCallum, M. (1969). *J. Mol. Biol.* **40**, 423.

Galau, G. A., Britten, R. J., and Davidson, E. H. (1974). *Cell* **2**, 9.

Georgiev, G. P. (1969). *J. Theor. Biol.* **25**, 473.

Georgiev, G. P. (1972). *Curr. Top. Develop. Biol.* **7**, 1.

Georgiev, G. P., Varshavsky, A. J., Ryskov, A. P., and Church, R. B. (1974). *Cold Spring Harbor Symp. Quant. Biol.* **38**, 869.

Giudice, G., and Mutolo, V. (1967). *Biochim. Biophys. Acta* **138**, 276.

Giudice, G., Sconzo, G., Ramirez, F., and Albanese, I. (1972). *Biochim. Biophys. Acta* **262**, 401.

Glisin, V. R., and Glisin, M. V. (1964). *Proc. Nat. Acad. Sci. U.S.* **52**, 1548.

Glisin, V. R., Glisin, M. V., and Doty, P. (1966). *Proc. Nat. Acad. Sci. U.S.* **56**, 285.

Goldberg R. B., Galau, G. A., Britten, R. J., and Davidson, E. H. (1973). *Proc. Nat. Acad. Sci. U.S.* **70**, 3516.

Graham, D. E., Neufeld, B. R., Davidson, E. H., and Britten, R. J. (1974). *Cell* **1**, 127.

Greenberg, J. R., and Perry, R. P. (1971). *J. Cell Biol.* **50**, 774.

Gross, K., Jacobs-Lorena, M., Baglioni, C., and Gross, P. R. (1973). *Proc. Nat. Acad. Sci. U.S.* **70**, 2614.

Gross, P. R. (1967). *Curr. Top. Develop. Biol.* **2**, 1.

Gross, P. R., and Cousineau, G. H. (1963). *Biochem. Biophys. Res. Commun.* **10**, 321.

Hansen, J. N., Spiegelman, G., and Halvorson, H. O. (1970). *Science* **168**, 1291.

Hartman, J. F., and Comb. D. G. (1969). *J. Mol. Biol.* **41**, 155.

Harvey, E. B. (1940). *Biol. Bull.* **78**, 412.

Hinegardner, R. (1968) *Amer. Nat* **102**, 517.

Hogan, B., and Gross, P. R. (1972). *Exp. Cell Res.* **72**, 101.

Holmes, D. S., and Bonner, J. (1974a). *Biochemistry* **13**, 841.

Holmes, D. S., and Bonner, J. (1974b). *Proc. Nat. Acad. Sci. U.S.* **71**, 1108.

Hörstadius, S. (1939). *Biol. Rev. Cambridge Phil. Soc.* **14**, 132.

Hough, B. R., and Davidson, E. H. (1972). *J. Mol. Biol.* **70**, 491.

Hoyer, B. H., McCarthy, B. J., and Bolton, E. T. (1964). *Science* **144**, 959.

Hynes, R. O., and Gross, P. R. (1972). *Biochim. Biophys. Acta* **259**, 104.

Hynes, R. O., Raff, R. A., and Gross, P. R. (1972a). *Develop. Biol.* **27**, 150.

Hynes, R. O., Greenhouse, G. A., Minkoff, F., and Gross, P. R. (1972b). *Develop. Biol.* **27**, 457.

Ilan, J., and Ilan, J. (1973). *Proc. Nat. Acad. Sci. U.S.* **70**, 1355.

Infante, A. A., and Nemer, M. (1968). *J. Mol. Biol.* **32**, 543.

Jelinek, W., Molloy, G., Fernandez-Munoz, R., Salditt, M., and Darnell, J. E. (1974). *J. Mol. Biol.* **82**, 361.

Kafiani, C. (1970). *Advan. Morphog.* **8**, 209.

Karasaki, S. (1968). *Exp. Cell Res.* **52**, 13.

Karp, G. C., and Whiteley, A. H. (1973). *Exp. Cell Res.* **78**, 236.

Kedes, L. H., and Birnstiel, M. L. (1971). *Nature (London)* **230**, 165.

Kedes, L. H., and Gross, P. R. (1969). *Nature (London)* **223**, 1335.

Kennell, D. E. (1971). *Progr. Nucl. Acid Res. Mol. Biol.* **11**, 259.

Kijima, S., and Wilt, F. H. (1969). *J. Mol. Biol.* **40**, 235.

Klein, W. H., Murphy, W., Attardi, G., Britten, R. J., and Davidson, E. H. (1974). *Proc. Nat. Acad. Sci. U.S.* **71**, 1785.

Kohne, D. E. (1970). *Quart. Rev. Biophys.* **3**, 327.

Kung, C. S. (1974). *Develop. Biol.* **36**, 343.

Laird, C. D. (1973). *Annu. Rev. Genet.* **7**, 177.

Lambert, B. (1974). *Cold Spring Harbor Symp. Quant. Biol.* **38**, 637.

Lee, Y., Mendecki, J., and Brawerman, G. (1971). *Proc. Nat. Acad. Sci. U.S.* **68**, 1331.

Levner, M. H. (1974). *Exp. Cell Res.* **85**, 296.

Lodish, H. F., Firtel, R. A., and Jacobson, A. (1974). *Cold Spring Harbor Symp. Quant. Biol.* **38**, 899.

Longo, F. J. (1972). *J. Morphol.* **138**, 207.

Lukanidin, E. M., Zalmanson, E. S.. Komaromi. L., Samarina, O. P., and Georgiev, G. P. (1972). *Nature (London) New Biol.* **238**, 193.

McCarthy, B. J., and Church, R. B. (1970). *Annu. Rev. Biochem.* **39**, 131.

McCarthy, B. J., and Farquhar, M. N. (1972). *In* "Evolution of Genetic Systems" (H. H. Smith, ed.), p. 1. Gordon & Breach, New York.

McCarthy, B. J., and McConaughy, B. L. (1968). *Biochem. Genet.* **2**, 37.

Mackintosh, F. R., and Bell, E. (1969). *Science* **164**, 961.

McLean, K. W., and Whiteley, A. H. (1974). *Exp. Cell Res.* **87**, 132.

Makino, S. (1956). "A Review of the Chromosome Numbers in Animals." Hokuryuka, Tokyo.

Marsh, L., and McCarthy, B. J. (1973). *Biochem. Biophys. Res. Commun.* **55**, 805.

Martin, T., Billings, P., Levey, A., Ozarslan, S., Quinlan, T., Swift, H., and Urbas, L. (1974). *Cold Spring Harbor Symp. Quant. Biol.* **38**, 921.

Millonig, G., Bosco, M., and Giambertone, L. (1968). *J. Exp. Zool.* **169**, 293.

Mizuno, S., and Macgregor, H. C. (1974). *Chromosoma* **48**, 239.

Mizuno, S., Whiteley, H. R., and Whiteley, A. H. (1973). *Differentiation* **1**, 339.

Mizuno, S., Lee, Y. R., Whiteley, A. H., and Whiteley, H. R. (1974). *Develop. Biol.* **37**, 18.

Molloy, G., Jelinek, W., Salditt, M., and Darnell, J. E. (1974). *Cell* **1**, 43.

Moore, A. R. (1913). *Arch. Entwicklungsmech. Organismen* **37**, 28.

Moore, P. C. (1966). "Treatise on Invertebrate Paleontology. Part U. Echinodermata," pp. U270-U297. Univ. of Kansas Press, Lawrence.

Morgan, T. H. (1927). "Experimental Embryology," pp. 493–501. Columbia Univ. Press, New York.

Mutolo, V., and Giudice, G. (1967). *Biochim. Biophys. Acta* **149**, 291.

Nakano, E., and Monroy, A. (1958). *Exp. Cell Res.* **14**, 236.

Nemer, M. (1967). *Progr. Nucl. Acid Res. Mol. Biol.* **17**, 243.

Nemer, M., and Lindsay, D. T. (1969). *Biochem. Biophys. Res. Commun.* **35**, 156.

Neyfakh, A. A. (1971). *Curr. Top. Develop. Biol.* **6**, 45.

Noronha, J. M., Sheys, G. H., and Buchanan, J. M. (1972). *Proc. Nat. Acad. Sci. U.S.* **69**, 2006.

Okazaki, K. (1975). *Amer. Zool.* **15**(3).

O'Melia, A. F., and Villee, C. A. (1972). *Nature (London), New Biol.* **239**, 51.

Ozaki, H. (1966). Ph.D. Thesis, Department of Zoology, University of Washington, Seattle.

Ozaki, H. (1971). *Develop. Biol.* **26**, 209.

Ozaki, H. (1975). *In* "Isozymes" (C. Markert, ed.), Vol. 3: Developmental Biology. p. 543.

Ozaki, H., and Whiteley, A. H. (1970). *Develop. Biol.* **21**, 196.

Patterson, J. B., and Stafford, D. W. (1970). *Biochemistry* **9**, 1278.

Patterson, J. B., and Stafford, D. W. (1971). *Biochemistry* **10**, 2775.

Paul, J. (1970). *Curr. Top. Develop. Biol.* **5**, 317.

Pederson, T. (1974). *J. Mol. Biol.* **83**, 163.

Peltz, R. (1973). *Biochim. Biophy. Acta* **308**, 148.

Perry, R. P., and Kelley, D. E. (1974). *Cell* **1**, 37.

Raff, R. A. (1975). *Amer. Zool.* **15**(3).

Raff, R. A., Greenhouse, G., Gross, K. W., and Gross, P. R. (1971). *J. Cell Biol.* **50**, 516.

Raff, R. A., Colot, H. V., Selvig, S. E., and Gross, P. R. (1972). *Nature (London)* **235**, 211.

Rinaldi, A. M., and Monroy, A. (1969). *Develop. Biol.* **19**, 73.

Ruderman, J. V., Baglioni, C., and Gross, P. R. (1974). *Nature (London)* **247**, 36.

Sachs, M. I., and Anderson, E. (1970). *J. Cell Biol.* **47**, 140.

Schultz, G. A., and Church, R. B. (1975). *In* "The Biochemistry of Animal Development" (R. Weber, ed.), Vol. 3: Molecular Aspects of Development. Academic Press, New York (in press).

Sconzo, G., and Giudice, G. (1971). *Biochim. Biophys. Acta* **254**, 447.

Sconzo, G., Vitrano, E., Bono, A., Di Giovanni, L., Mutolo, V., and Giudice, G. (1971). *Biochim. Biophys. Acta* **232**, 132.

Selvig, S. E., Greenhouse, G. A., and Gross, P. R. (1972). *Cell Differentiation* **1**, 5.

Skoultchi, A., and Gross, P. R. (1973). *Proc. Nat. Acad. Sci. U.S.* **70**, 2840.

Slater, D. W., and Spiegelman, S. (1966). *Proc. Nat. Acad. Sci. U.S.* **56**, 164.

Slater, D. W., and Spiegelman, S. (1968). *Biochim. Biophys. Acta* **166**, 82.

Slater, D. W., and Spiegelman, S. (1970). *Biochim. Biophys. Acta* **254**, 447.

Slater, D. W., Slater, I., and Gillespie, D. (1972). *Nature (London)* **240**, 333.

Slater, I., and Slater, D. W. (1972). *Nature (London), New Biol.* **237**, 81.

Slater, I., and Slater, D. W. (1974). *Proc. Nat. Acad. Sci. U.S.* **71**, 1103.

Slater, I., Gillespie, D., and Slater, D. W. (1973). *Proc. Nat. Acad. Sci. U.S.* **70**, 406.

Smith, M. J., Hough, B. R., Chamberlin, M. E., and Davidson, E. H. (1974). *J. Mol. Biol.* **85**, 103.

Spiegel, M., and Rubenstein, N. A. (1972). *Exp. Cell Res.* **70**, 423.

Spiegel, M, and Spiegel, E. S. (1975). *Amer. Zool.* **15**(3).

Spiegelman, G., Hansen, J. N., Whiteley, H. R., and Halvorson, H. O. (1975). In preparation.

Spirin, A. S. (1969). *Eur. J. Biochem.* **10**, 20.

Strathman, M. F. (1967). M.S. Thesis, Department of Zoology, University of Washington, Seattle.

Sy, J., and McCarty, K. S. (1968). *Biochim. Biophys. Acta* **166**, 571.

Sy, J., and McCarty, K. (1970). *Biochim. Biophys. Acta* **199**, 86.

Sy, J., and McCarty, K. S. (1971). *Biochim Biophys. Acta* **228**, 517.

Tennent, D. H. (1912). *J. Morphol.* **23**, 17.

Tennent, D. H. (1922). *Carnegie Inst. Wash. Publ.* **312**, 3.

Thomas, C. A., Jr., Pyeritz, R. E., Wilson, D. A., Dancus, B. M., Lee, C. S., Bick, M. D., Huane, H. L., and Zimm, B. H. (1974). *Cold Spring Harbor Symp. Quant. Biol.* **38**, 353.

Timourian, H. (1975). *Amer. Zool.* **15**(3).

Ullman, J., and McCarthy, B. J. (1973). *Biochim. Biophys. Acta* **294**, 405 and 416.

von Ledebur-Villiger, M. (1972). *Exp. Cell Res.* **72**, 285.

Walker, P. M. B. (1971). *Progr. Biophys. Mol. Biol.* **23**, 145.

Weinberg, E. S., Birnstiel, M. L., Purdom, J. F., and Williamson, R. (1972). *Nature (London)* **240**, 225.

Whiteley, A. H., and Chambers, E. L. (1966). *J. Cell Physiol.* **68**, 309.

Whiteley, A. H., and Whiteley, H. R. (1972). *Develop. Biol.* **29**, 183.

Whiteley, A. H., McCarthy, B. J., and Whiteley, H. R. (1966). *Proc. Nat. Acad. Sci. U.S.* **55**, 519.

Whiteley, H. R., McCarthy, B. J., and Whiteley, A. H. (1970). *Develop. Biol.* **21**, 216.

Whiteley, H. R., Mizuno, S., Lee, Y. R., and Whiteley, A. H. (1975). *Amer. Zool.* **15**, 141.

Wilson, D. A., and Thomas, C. A. (1974). *J. Mol. Biol.* **84**, 115.

Wilt, F. H. (1970). *Develop. Biol.* **23**, 444.

Wilt, F. H. (1973). *Proc. Nat. Acad. Sci. U.S.* **70**, 2345.

CHAPTER 4

REGULATION OF MESSENGER RNA TRANSLATION DURING INSECT DEVELOPMENT

Joseph Ilan and Judith Ilan

DEPARTMENT OF ANATOMY AND DEVELOPMENTAL BIOLOGY CENTER
SCHOOL OF MEDICINE
CASE WESTERN RESERVE UNIVERSITY
CLEVELAND, OHIO

I. Introduction

Insect metamorphosis is regarded as differentiation at the postembryonic level. We classify cells as differentiated on the basis of morphological qualities that are attributed primarily to structural proteins and to a lesser degree to enzyme proteins. It is highly probable that the process of cell differentiation is linked to the mechanisms that direct specific protein synthesis rather than with the ultimate appearance of protein molecules. Although we know that the appearance of specific message is regulated at the transcriptional level, the expression of the gene as a protein end product is also under regulation, which may prove to be a major event in cell differentiation. The mechanism of protein synthesis nearly completely overlaps in prokaryote and eukaryote species, although some differences do exist (Ilan and Ilan, 1973b); these differences appear to be variants of essentially the same mechanism. Thus, in insects initiation of the polypeptide chain occurs principally by the same mechanism responsible for initiation of mRNA translation in other eukaryotes and prokaryotes (Ilan and Ilan, 1971, 1973c; Ilan et al., 1972). Activation of amino acids is also similar to that of other organisms. This could be measured either as a pyrophosphate exchange reaction (Howells et al., 1967) or as formation of aminoacyl-tRNA (Ilan et al., 1970, 1972; Onodera and Komano, 1964). Reactions involving the elongation of polypeptide chain are also similar to those in other eukaryotes. This is evident from studies on amino acid incorporation in cell-free systems of insects (Fox et al., 1965; Ilan, 1968; Ilan and Lipmann, 1966). Also, the mechanism of chain termination is principally similar to that of other eukaryotes and prokaryotes. This involves the terminator codon UAA and a protein termination factor which releases the completed polypeptide chain from the mRNA complex in a manner similar to that in other organisms. (Ilan, 1971, 1973). It follows from the above discussion that the specificity in gene activity which brings about metamorphosis does not reside in differences in the protein synthesizing machinery between insects and other organisms. Thus, the mechanism of gene expression responsible for morphogenesis and metamorphosis must be of a general nature and not peculiar to insects.

The development of pupa into adult occurs in a differentiating system in which many changes take place, usually in one direction. In insects, growth and differentiation are regulated by several hormones. In larvae the brain hormone stimulates the prothoracic gland to secrete ecdysone. The latter, in the presence of juvenile hormone which is secreted from the corpora allata, causes another larval molt. The number of larval instars varies within and among species. At the end of larval life, the corpora allata cease to secrete juvenile hormone and the mature larva is left with a low concentration of hormone. Under these conditions, the response to high titer of ecdysone will bring about a pupal molt. At the end of pupation, when almost no juvenile hormone remains, epidermal cells respond to high titer of ecdysone by secreting adult cuticle (Schneiderman and Gilbert, 1964).

The development of pupa into adult can be regulated by juvenile hormone. Topical application of juvenile hormone or juvenile hormone mimics on first-day pupae of *Tenebrio molitor* brings about a second pupal molt 8 days later. Therefore, this system is most suitable for the study of gene expression mediated by hormone. The epidermis is one of the target tissues of juvenile hormone. Normally the pupa develops into an adult and the epidermis secretes a new adult cuticle that contains protein with a high content of tyrosine (Patel, 1972). When juvenile hormone is topically applied on first-day pupae, it brings about a second pupal molt and the epidermis secretes pupal cuticular protein different in its tyrosine content (low tyrosine) and its amino acid sequence. Therefore, such a system provides a useful tool for the study of involvement of juvenile hormone in morphogenesis and development and is useful in the study of molecular events that are under the influence of juvenile hormone. Thus the use of juvenile hormone serves the purpose of studying mechanisms of gene expression. We have found that the major influence of juvenile hormone in promoting the synthesis of the two classes of cuticular protein—adult and pupal—is at the translational level. This is facilitated by controlling the translation of cuticular mRNA. The translational control is mediated by the appearance of new rate-limiting aminoacyl-tRNA.

II. Steps Involved in Protein Synthesis

Since we shall be dealing primarily with reactions involving protein synthesis at the level of mRNA translation, the steps involved in protein synthesis are summarized in Fig. 1. For more detailed information, see Ilan and Ilan (1974).

III. Stability of mRNA for Cuticular Protein in *Tenebrio molitor*

One of the characteristics of the differentiated cell is its ability at one point in its development to synthesize a large amount of a specific protein. This is usually accomplished by production of "stable" (long-lived) mRNA. If a specific mRNA is stable, this amounts to amplification of this specific gene. A few examples of differentiating systems containing stable mRNA follow: the mammalian reticulocyte in which the mRNA for hemoglobin is synthesized much before translation begins (Marks *et al.*, 1963); sea urchin eggs which support protein synthesis after fertiliza-

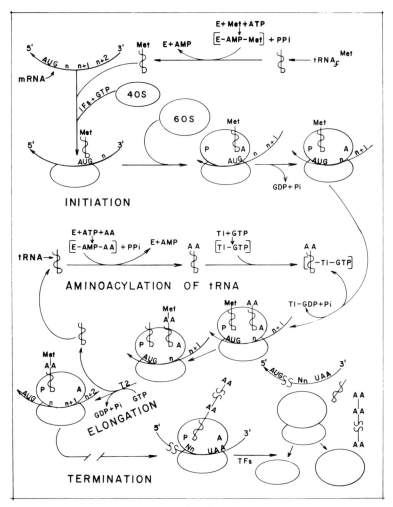

FIG. 1. Schematic outline of steps involved in peptide chain formation. AUG is the initiation codon which calls for methionine. The symbols n, $n+1$, and $n+2$ represent a series of adjacent codons in the mRNA segment shown; tRNA$_f^{Met}$ represents the initiator tRNA; IFs signifies initiation factors. T1 and T2 are transferase I and II, respectively, and Nn is the adjacent codon to the terminator codon UAA. This is the codon for the carboxyl end amino acid on the peptide. TFs stands for termination factors. From Ilan and Ilan (1974).

tion on maternal message through the blastula stage (Gross and Cousineau, 1963). During the development of slime molds mRNA for some enzymes is very stable (Sussman, 1966). Induction of glutamine synthetase in chick embryo retina results in accumulation of stable mRNA

(Moscona *et al.*, 1968). A long-lived mRNA for feather protein in the developing chick was described by Scott and Bell (1964); and for the crystalline lens proteins, by Stewart and Papaconstantinou (1967). In insects, stable mRNA was shown for adult cuticular protein synthesis in *Tenebrio* (Ilan and Quastel, 1966; Ilan, 1968, 1969b; Ilan *et al.*, 1970) and for cocoonase in differentiating zymogen cells of the glia gland of the silk moth (Kafatos and Reich, 1968). It is important to mention that the stability of mRNA is usually measured indirectly by assuming that stability of messenger is expressed as independence of protein synthesis from concomitant RNA synthesis. This is expressed as a decay of protein synthesis capacity upon exposure to inhibitors of RNA synthesis, such as actinomycin D. It is not known what controls mRNA stability. Evidence from mammalian tissues as well as from insect tissues (Kafatos and Reich, 1968) indicates that a diversity of mRNA half lives exist in a given tissue. Therefore, if a battery of genes is equally stimulated in terms of transcription during development by an agent such as a hormone, the expression of each gene, as monitored by the synthesis of the corresponding protein over time, may differ considerably. The synthesis of large amounts of differentiating protein over time, a process that characterizes differentiating cells, is a function of the stability of mRNA. Nothing is known about how mRNA is stabilized.

In some cases involving stable mRNA there is a lag period between its synthesis and the time of translation. This is documented for maternal mRNA in sea urchin oocytes, hemoglobin mRNA and mRNA for adult cuticular protein in *Tenebrio*. In these cases the mRNA is synthesized and stored for later translation.

In early experiments we followed the inhibition of RNA synthesis during the metamorphosis of *Tenebrio*. Actinomycin D was injected into pupae in doses sufficient to inhibit RNA synthesis almost completely. Though this treatment caused abnormal development, most of the adult cuticular protein was synthesized (Ilan *et al.*, 1966). Since the drug is known to inhibit DNA-dependent synthesis of RNA, the synthesis of adult cuticular protein was an indication, but not a proof, of the presence of stable template for this protein.

The experiment with actinomycin D suggests not only that mRNA for cuticular protein is stable, but also that it is not immediately translated—indicating translational control. Translation regulation must be mediated by a rate-limiting step of the protein-synthesizing machinery. Therefore, individual reactions leading to polypeptide synthesis should be investigated in order to elucidate a rate-limiting reaction. For this reason we developed a cell-free system for protein synthesis. In such a system each individual reaction leading to the synthesis of the polypeptide product could be delineated and the possible rate-limiting step identified.

IV. Regulation of Cuticular mRNA Translation in Cell-Free Systems from *Tenebrio* Pupae

A. tRNA AND ITS ACTIVATING ENZYMES ARE THE LIMITING FACTORS IN THE MICROSOMAL CELL-FREE SYSTEM

A cell-free system capable of incorporating amino acids into protein-utilizing microsomes or ribosomes containing the endogenous mRNA was developed (Ilan and Lipmann, 1966; Ilan, 1968). A typical microsomal amino acid incorporating system is given in Table I.

TABLE I

PROPERTIES OF MICROSOMAL SYSTEM[a]

Incubation system	Incorporation of leucine-^{14}C (cpm/mg RNA)
Complete	4,260
Without ATP and its regenerating system	102
Without GTP	150
Without amino acids	1,685
With supernatant fluid	4,350
With RNase, 25 μg/ml	50
With puromycin ($4 \times 10^{-4} M$)	406
With *Escherichia coli* supernatant fluid	12,750
With rabbit liver supernatant fluid	15,360
Complete (0° control)	80
Without microsomes	20
Without Mg^{2+}	45

[a] For experimental conditions, see Ilan (1968).

It can be seen that the system has an absolute requirement for microsomal particles, for ATP and its regenerating system, for GTP, and for magnesium ions. Insect supernatant fluid does not stimulate, but supernatant fractions from *E. coli* or rabbit liver stimulate the system about 3-fold. There are at least two possible interpretations for the above stimulation: (1) that the supernatant fluid provides tRNA and amino acid-activating enzymes which are both limiting; the amino acid is then transferred from tRNA into protein, since, as observed by Nathans and Lipmann (1960), once tRNA is aminoacylated the source of aminoacyl tRNA is not important; (2) that the insect microsomes might contain a limiting amount of transfer factors supplied by the supernatant fraction of *E. coli* or rat liver. The second possibility was proved to be incorrect by the following experiment: tRNA charged with 19 ^{12}C-labeled amino acids, and leucine-^{14}C was incubated with insect microsomes. Under such conditions the transfer reaction is studied separately and is uncoupled from the activation and charging of tRNA. Table II shows that the trans-

TABLE II

REQUIREMENTS OF AMINOACYL-tRNA TRANSFER SYSTEM ON MICROSOMES[a]

Additions and omissions	Radioactivity transferred (cpm/mg microsomal RNA)
None	536
With liver supernatant fluid	526
With *E. coli* supernatant fluid	232
With 2×10^{-4} M puromycin	30
With leucine-^{12}C (4 mM)	558
With liver supernatant fluid and leucine-^{12}C	510
With *E. coli* supernatant fluid and leucine-^{12}C	302
With insect supernatant fluid	558
Without microsomes	18
Without microsomes; with *E. coli* supernatant fluid	20
Without microsomes; with liver supernatant fluid	20
Without microsomes; with insect supernatant fluid	16
Without GTP	14
Without Mg^{2+}	12

[a] The reaction mixture and conditions were as described by Ilan (1968). Each tube contained 0.35 mg of tRNA charged with 19 ^{12}C-labeled amino acids and leucine-^{14}C, 1700 cpm per tube. The concentration of protein in the supernatant fluid was 1.6 μg/ml.

fer reaction was neither stimulated by rabbit liver supernatant fluid nor by insect supernatant fluid. *E. coli* supernatant fluid was inhibitory probably because of the presence of nucleases.

Other features of the transfer reaction of leucine from transfer RNA to polypeptide are also shown. Inhibition by puromycin is almost complete and there is absolute dependency on GTP and Mg^{2+}. Leucine-^{12}C has no effect on the transfer reaction; this indicates unidirection of the reaction and that there is no recharging of tRNA, which would bring about isotopic dilution and a significant decrease in incorporation. These experiments rule out the second possibility that the transferases are limiting the system and point to the fact that the microsomes are saturated with transfer enzymes and are not influenced by the addition of supernatant fluid from *Tenebrio*.

The stimulation is due to tRNA and its activating enzyme, which are rate-limiting factors in the protein-synthesizing system. The evidence is presented in Table III. For these studies supernatnat fluid from *E.*

TABLE III

Stimulation of ^{14}C-Leucine Incorporation on Insect Microsomes by *Escherichia coli* Supernatant Fluid and *E. coli* tRNA[a,b]

Additions	Incorporation (cpm/mg microsomal RNA)
None	1240
With *E. coli* tRNA	1200
With *E. coli* tRNA and *E. coli* supernatant fluid	6300
With *E. coli* supernatant fluid	1230
With *E. coli* supernatant fluid and tRNA (less microsomes)	18
With *E. coli* supernatant fluid and tRNA (0° control)	45

[a] From Ilan (1968).
[b] Incubation was carried out for 8 minutes at 30°C. *E. coli* supernatant fluid free of tRNA was used. tRNA and *E. coli* supernatant proteins were at levels of 3 mg/ml and 1.6 mg/ml, respectively, when added.

coli containing all amino acid activating enzymes for 20 amino acids was obtained free of tRNA by passage through DEAE-cellulose. Neither this supernatant fluid alone nor *E. coli* tRNA alone could stimulate protein synthesis on insect microsomes above the endogeneous level. However, when both were added together, 5-fold stimulation of leucine incorporation into protein was observed. These experiments indicate that the limiting factor in the *Tenebrio* protein synthesizing system is tRNA and its amino acid-activating enzyme. Therefore, a ribosomal cell-free system from *Tenebrio* showing complete dependency on tRNA and enzyme fraction was prepared. This system could promote incorporation of amino acids utilizing endogenous mRNA (Ilan, 1968; Ilan *et al.*, 1970).

From the experiments with actinomycin D we deduced that the mRNA for cuticular protein is stable and exists on ribosomes at an early developmental stage and is translated 5 to 6 days later. Moreover, microsomes isolated from late adult development but not from early development are capable of synthesis of protein with a relatively high tyrosine content (Ilan and Lipmann, 1966). Since microsomes contain all the necessary factors for protein synthesis, factors associated with translational control of adult cuticular protein synthesis may be obtained from microsomes when this protein is being synthesized. It follows that the regulation of the synthesis involves a rate-limiting component of the protein-synthesizing machinery. We have already seen that tRNA and amino acid-activating enzymes are rate-limiting in the microsomal amino acid incorporation system.

B. TRANSLATION OF ENDOGENOUS mRNA FOR ADULT CUTICULAR PROTEIN WITH RIBOSOMES FROM EARLY DEVELOPMENT

Ribosomes containing the endogenous mRNA and capable of protein synthesis have been prepared from microsomes. These ribosomes were purified to an extent that made them completely dependent on supernatant enzymes and tRNA for incorporation activity. The supernatant enzyme was extracted from microsomes and was prepared free from tRNA. tRNA was prepared from pupae or developing adults at different time periods after the larval pupal molt.

Cuticular protein is synthesized *in vivo* 5–6 days after the larval pupal molt. As an approximation for cuticular protein synthesis in ribosomal preparations, we measured ratios of tyrosine to leucine incorporation. An increase in such a ratio may indicate preferential adult cuticular protein synthesis. Experiments of this nature are summarized in Table IV.

When ribosomes from day 1 were used and the enzyme fraction and tRNA were from day 7, a relatively high ratio of incorporation of tyrosine to leucine was observed. Both enzyme and tRNA must be from day 7 in order to obtain a high level of tyrosine incorporation, for when a combination such as enzyme from day 7 and tRNA from day 1, or enzyme from day 1 and tRNA from day 7 were used, a relatively low ratio of tyrosine to leucine was observed. It is important to emphasize that the low ratio is a result of decreasing tyrosine incorporation without affecting incorporation of leucine. The incorporation of the latter is at the same level under all conditions in which the source of tRNA and enzyme were varied. The salient point of these experiments is that under conditions in which both enzyme and tRNA from day 7 are used to supplement the ribosomal protein synthesizing system, a protein product is synthesized which contains more tyrosine per leucine per mole of product, and therefore it is qualitatively different.

Table IV also shows the complete dependency of the ribosomal preparation on the addition of tRNA and enzyme for incorporation activity. When ribosomes from day 7 were used, essentially the same results were obtained, namely, that both tRNA and enzyme from day 7 are needed for the translation of message into protein with high tyrosine content. The higher ratio obtained on day 7 ribosomes in comparison to day 1 ribosomes is interpreted to result from a higher content of messenger for cuticular protein on day 7 ribosomes. However, both ribosomes from day

TABLE IV

Ratio of Tyrosine Incorporation to Leucine Incorporation[a]

Enzyme		tRNA		Tyrosine (cpm/mg RNA)	Leucine (cpm/mg RNA)	Tyrosine to leucine ratio
Day 1	Day 7	Day 1	Day 7			
Ribosomes from day 1 pupae						
	+	+		9,600	9,800	0.98
+			+	2,400	9,800	0.25
		+		130	150	
	+	+	+	2,200	10,200	0.21
+			+	2,500	9,600	0.26
	+			38	42	
+				45	51	
Ribosomes from day 7 pupae						
	+	+		17,600	10,700	1.64
+			+	2,600	10,600	0.25
		+		120	200	
	+	+	+	2,000	9,900	0.23
+			+	2,400	11,600	0.21
	+			50	48	
+				46	52	

[a] The reaction mixture (0.25 ml) consisted of: 0.5 mg of ribosomal RNA of insect ribosomes; 0.5 mM GTP; 8 mM dithiothreitol; 2 mM ATP; 8 mM phosphoenolpyruvate; 40 μg of pyruvate kinase per milliliter; 40 mM KCl; 35 mM Tris-HCl, pH 7.6; 6 mM MgCl$_2$; 19 ^{12}C-labeled amino acids, 0.06 mM each; 0.2 μCi of leucine-^{14}C (222 mCi/mmole) or tyrosine-^{14}C (375 mCi/mmole); 1 mM phenylthiourea; 2 mg of enzyme protein, 1 mg of tRNA per milliliter. Incubations were carried out for 30 minutes at 30°C (Ilan *et al.*, 1970).

1 or day 7 translate a protein with high tyrosine content when supplemented with tRNA and enzyme from day 7.

If synthesis of protein with high tyrosine content represents adult cuticular protein, it implies that ribosomes from day 1 pupae contain the message for this protein. The translation of this message is controlled by tRNA and enzyme fraction. With *Tenebrio* it was observed that when juvenile hormone or its mimics (such as dodecyl methyl ether) are topically applied to day 1 pupae, one can obtain a second pupal molt 8 days later (Ilan *et al.*, 1970). When dodecyl methyl ether was applied (1 μl per pupa) on day 1 pupa (0–4 hours after emergence) a perfect second pupal molt was obtained. It was important to determine whether the newly synthesized pupal cuticular protein results from a mechanism in which juvenile hormone affects the enzyme fraction and tRNA.

C. INVOLVEMENT OF JUVENILE HORMONE IN REGULATION OF mRNA TRANSLATION

Ribosomes prepared from animals 7 days after the larval pupal molt were used in the experiments utilizing juvenile hormone, since these ribosomes have more mRNA than ribosomes from day 1 pupae. As juvenile hormone we used dodecyl methyl ether. In one set of experiments the ribosomes were prepared from untreated animals. These ribosomes were supplemented with tRNA and an enzyme preparation from hormone-treated animals. Extractions of enzyme and tRNA were made 6 days after treatment. The results are summarized in Table V.

TABLE V

EFFECT OF tRNA FROM HORMONE-TREATED ANIMALS[a]

| Day 1 | Enzyme | | tRNA (from day 7 pupae) | | Tyrosine (cpm/mg RNA) | Leucine (cpm/mg RNA) |
| | Day 7 | | From hormone-treated animals | From normal animals | | |
	Normal	Hormone				
Normal ribosomes						
	+		+		2,600	11,000
	+			+	18,000	10,800
+				+	2,000	9,500
+			+		2,400	11,500
		+	+		2,100	11,100
		+		+	2,300	11,000
Ribosomes from hormone-treated animals						
	+		+		2,400	11,800
	+			+	17,200	10,500
		+	+		2,200	11,200
		+		+	2,400	10,000
+				+	2,600	10,500
+			+		2,400	11,600

[a] Ribosomes from normal or hormone-treated animals were used 7 days after the pupal molt. tRNA was prepared from animals of the same age (normal) or from insects of the same age which had been treated with dodecyl methyl ether (1 μl per pupa) on their first day of pupal life (Ilan *et al.*, 1970).

Essentially, the table shows that tRNA and enzyme from hormone-treated animals separately or in combination suppress the incorporation of tyrosine without affecting the incorporation of leucine. In contrast, tRNA and enzyme from 7-day-old untreated animals together promote a higher incorporation of tyrosine. Again, tRNA and enzyme from hormone-treated animals supplemented to ribosomes from normal pupae, shifted the pattern of incorporation into protein which contains fewer tyrosine units per leucine. The shift in incorporation is determined by the tRNA and the enzyme fraction only, since day 7 ribosomes from hormone-treated animals behave as normal ribosomes and can promote different patterns of incorporation in response to varying the sources of tRNA and enzyme. This is illustrated in Table V.

D. Characterization of the Translational Product with High Tyrosine Content as Adult Cuticular Protein

Changes in the ratio of tyrosine to leucine incorporation in a cell-free preparation can serve only as an indicator, but not as proof for a shift in protein synthesis. Therefore, a more rigorous test was conducted which involved fingerprinting of the proteins as follows. Adult cuticular protein was labeled *in vivo* by injecting leucine-^{14}C into animals during the late adult developmental stage. The animals were allowed to develop into adults and the adult cuticular protein was isolated. This labeled protein was combined with leucyl-^{3}H-labeled protein synthesized in a cell-free preparation under conditions that showed high tyrosine to leucine ratio of amino acid incorporation. The combined proteins were digested with trypsin, and the tryptic digest was subjected to column chromatography. Trypsin specifically cleaves the polypeptide chain at points where lysine occurs. Therefore, if the protein synthesized *in vitro* is the same as that synthesized *in vivo*, the peptides resulting from the tryptic digestion would be identical in length, in amino acid composition, and hence in charge. Cochromatography of the tryptic digest of the *in vivo* and *in vitro* protein products should show the same elution pattern for the ^{14}C-labeled peptides synthesized *in vivo* and the ^{3}H-labeled peptides synthesized *in vitro*.

Almost identical elution patterns were obtained when a digest of labeled protein synthesized in a cell-free system was cochromatographed with a digest of labeled cuticular protein synthesized *in vivo* (Ilan, 1969b; Ilan *et al.*, 1970). This is illustrated in Fig. 2a.

We have seen in Table V that addition of tRNA from day 7 animals which had been treated with juvenile hormone on day 1, is sufficient to bring about a shift in the ratio of amino acids incorporated into protein in cell-free preparations. A protein synthesized under such conditions and labeled with leucine-^{3}H was combined with leucyl-^{14}C-labeled peptide that was synthesized with enzyme and tRNA from day-7 animals. Both peptides were trypsinized and cochromatographed on a Dowex 50-X2 col-

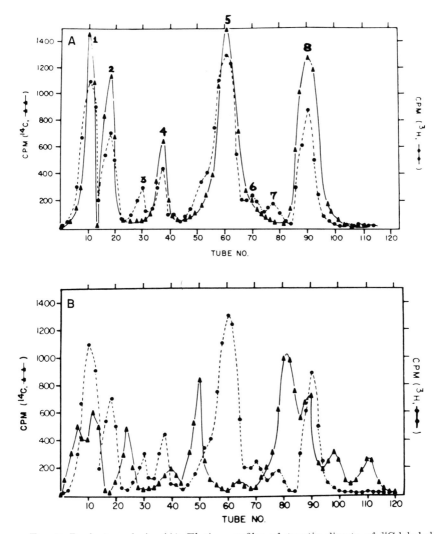

FIG. 2. Product analysis. (A) Elution profiles of tryptic digests of ^{14}C-labeled cuticular protein synthesized *in vivo* and digest of ^{3}H-labeled protein synthesized *in vitro*. The digests were cochromatographed. The *in vitro* incubation medium contained tRNA and enzyme from day 7 untreated animals. (B) Elution profiles of tryptic digests of ^{3}H-labeled protein synthesized *in vitro* as in (A) and tryptic digest of ^{14}C-labeled protein which had been synthesized with tRNA from hormone-treated animals. Both digests were cochromatographed. From Ilan *et al.* (1970, 1972.)

umn by a gradient of pyridinium acetate as described above. Figure 2b shows that the profile of the leucyl-^{3}H-labeled peptide does not correspond in position after chromatography with the profile of the leucyl-^{14}C-labeled peptide which represents fragments of adult cuticular protein. The only difference between the two preparations lies in the source of tRNA.

It appears that the tRNA from hormone-treated animals can selectively translate mRNA which is not adult cuticular protein. Also, it is obvious that the message for adult cuticular protein is present in the preparation. Similar results to those obtained with tRNA from hormone-treated animals were obtained with tRNA from day 1 animals (Ilan, 1969b; Ilan et al., 1970).

E. The Role of tRNA in Translational Control

We have already seen that tRNA is a rate-limiting component in the microsomal cell-free system. In the purified ribosomal system, addition of tRNA from the more differentiated stage brings about a shift in the ratio of amino acid incorporation (Table IV) which has proved to be a shift to the synthesis of adult cuticular protein (Fig. 2). However, since the tRNA fraction is crude, it is possible that other components in the tRNA fraction are responsible for the shift in protein synthesis.

For this reason we designed a series of experiments which are summarized in Table VI.

The table shows that addition to ribosomes of 0.5 mg of tRNA from day 1 pupae is saturating, since addition of 1 mg does not promote greater incorporation for leucine or tyrosine. However, when 0.5 mg of day 1 tRNA was added together with 1 mg of tRNA from day 7 pupae, the ratio of tyrosine to leucine incorporation increased, producing an approximately 6-fold stimulation in tyrosine incorporation over and above the saturation level of day 1 tRNA.

One feature shared by all tRNAs studied is that the primary structure terminates in a CCA sequence at the 3' end, the amino acid acceptor end. Therefore, experiments were designed to cleave the CCA terminal end of tRNA, making it ineffective and thus ascertaining that the stimulatory activity is indeed due to the tRNA. For this reason the enzyme tRNA-CMP-AMP-pyrophosphorylase was prepared from rat liver. This enzyme cleaved the three terminal nucleotides as follows:

$$\text{tRNA-C-C-A} + \text{PP}_i \rightleftarrows \text{tRNA} + 2\text{CTP} + \text{ATP}$$

The reaction is reversible and can be driven in either direction by varying concentrations of the components of the reaction mixture. Table VII shows the strict specificity of the enzyme for tRNA. The enzyme

TABLE VI

EFFECT OF tRNA WHICH HAD BEEN INACTIVATED BY PYROPHOSPHOROLYSIS
AND REACTIVATED ON AMINO ACID INCORPORATION[a,b]

Addition of tRNA (mg)				Incorporation	
	From day 7				
From day 1	Untreated	Pyrophos- phorylized	Pyrophos- phorylized and re- activated	Tyrosine (cpm/mg RNA)	Leucine (cpm/mg RNA)
—	1.0	—	—	18,000	10,000
0.5	—	—	—	2,300	10,700
1.0	—	—	—	2,500	10,100
0.5	1.0	—	—	12,600	9,900
0.5	—	1.0	—	2,100	11,200
0.5	—	—	1.0	11,700	10,600
0.5	—	—	1.0[c]	2,200	10,400

[a] From Ilan et al. (1970, 1972).

[b] Pyrophosphorolysis of tRNA prepared from animals 7 days after larval pupal molt was carried out (Ilan et al., 1970). Reactivation was carried out in 3 ml at 37°C for 60 minutes. The reaction mixture contained 40 mM Tris-HCl (pH 8.4), 6 mM MgCl$_2$, 0.5 mM ATP, 0.5 mM CTP, 10 mM phosphoenolpyruvate, 5 µg of pyruvate kinase, 5 µg of inorganic pyrophorphorylase, 3 mg of pyrophosphorylized tRNA, and 3 mg of rat liver tRNA-CMP-AMP-pyrophosphorylase. The reaction was terminated by the addition of an equal volume of water-saturated phenol, and tRNA was isolated. Experimental conditions for amino acid incorporation were as described in the legend to Table IV except that the ribosomes and enzyme used were prepared only from animals 7 days after the larval pupal molt. The total volume of the reaction mixture was reduced to 0.1 ml and tRNA was added as indicated in the table.

[c] Reactivation reaction of pyrophosphorylized tRNA was carried out in the absence of CTP.

released practically no nucleotides from ribosomal or 5 S RNA and was very active with tRNA.

In Table VI it is shown that addition of tRNA from day 7 to ribosomes saturated with tRNA from day 1 brought about a shift in protein synthesis which was expressed as a 6-fold increase in tyrosine incorporation. However, when day 7 tRNA was treated with tRNA-C-C-A-pyrophosphorylase to cleave its terminal CCA end nucleotides, reisolated, and then used, it failed to bring about the shift in protein synthesis (Table VII).

These results suggest but do not prove the involvement of tRNA. Since it is a possibility that the day 7 tRNA fraction carries with it

TABLE VII

SPECIFICITY OF RAT LIVER
tRNA-CMP-AMP-Pyrophosphorylase[a-c]

RNA fraction, 1 mg/ml	Nucleotides adsorbed to Norit (cpm)
Ribosomal	0
5 S	100
tRNA	125,300

[a] From Ilan *et al.* (1970).

[b] The enzyme was prepared from rat liver by the method of Canellakis and Herbert (1960). Incubation was for 2 hours at 37°C in a total volume of 1 ml containing 0.2 µl of $^{32}PP_i$ (6 µmoles), 6 µmoles of Tris-HCl (pH 7.6), 10 µmoles of KF, 1 mg of enzyme protein per milliliter, and 1 mg of RNA. The incubation was terminated by the addition of 1 ml of cold suspension of charcoal in $HClO_4$ (10 parts of 2.5% perchloric acid and 1 part of 10%, w/w, aqueous suspension of Norit). After 10 minutes at 0° and occasional stirring, the charcoal suspension was transferred onto a Millipore filter and washed six times with 20 ml of H_2O. The filters were placed in vials, dried, and counted in a liquid scintillation system.

[c] Ribonuclease activity was not detected in the enzyme preparation.

a small amount of mRNA, it is possible also to assume that the tRNA-pyrophosphorylase is contaminated with some ribonuclease that will degrade the mRNA in the tRNA fraction. Our assay system is geared to detect pyrophosphorylase, and it failed to detect ribonuclease. Therefore, day 7 tRNA was stripped from its 3′ CCA end nucleotides and reisolated. This tRNA had no stimulatory activity. It was then reactivated by reversing the reaction and reattaching the CCA end nucleotides. This reactivated tRNA was isolated and, as can be seen in Table VII, it regained its ability to stimulate relative tyrosine incorporation over and above the saturation of day 1 tRNA. Therefore, it is the tRNA, but not a contaminant accompanying the tRNA fraction, which is the important factor in bringing about the selection in mRNA translation.

F. A POSSIBLE INVOLVEMENT OF tRNA[Leu] AND ITS ACTIVATING ENZYME IN REGULATION OF mRNA TRANSLATION

There is a growing volume of evidence indicating that alteration of isoaccepting tRNA occurs during development and differentiation (Lee and Ingram, 1967; Holland *et al.*, 1967; Taylor *et al.*, 1967, 1971; Mittelman, 1971; Yang, 1971; Yang and Novelli, 1968). There are more isoacceptor-tRNA species in embryonic forms of tissues than in adult tissue. There is also suggestive evidence that the number of aminoacyl tRNA synthetases and their activities might vary with the age of the tissue. During the development of *Rana pipiens,* tRNA from early and late embryonic stages aminoacylate most efficiently with synthetases from the homologous stage. Therefore, differences must have existed in both the tRNA and the synthetase preparations (Caston, 1971). These various findings agree with the hypothesis that differentiation is associated with changes in isoacceptor-tRNA subspecies with consequent codon restriction (Strehler *et al.,* 1967).

It was reported that in a differentiating cell system of calf lens (Virmaux *et al.,* 1969) a direct correlation between the relative amount of the aminoacyl-tRNAs and the amino acid composition of the crystallins exists. A similar correlation was found in the posterior part of the silk gland of *Bombyx mori* (Garel *et al.,* 1970). They found a linear correlation between the amino acid distribution of the fibroin and the corresponding tRNAs acylated during the secretion phase. Therefore, it appears that in the silk gland there is a functional adaptation of the tRNA level to the amino acids incorporated into fibroin. In the liver of laying hens, at the time of synthesis of phosvitin (a yolk protein which contains 50% serine), there is an increase in the amount of seryl-tRNA (Bernfield and Mäenäpä, 1971).

In *Tenebrio* there is a correlation between the timing of the appearance of the new tRNA[Leu] and its activating enzyme and the switch in protein synthesis. We have observed a change in aminoacylation of tRNA[Leu] at the time when the pupa commences cuticular protein synthesis *in vivo.* For these studies tRNA was isolated either at day 1 or at day 7 after the larval pupal molt. Leucyl-tRNA synthetase was partially purified from day 1 and day 7. Taking the enzyme and tRNA from day 1 or from day 7, the kinetics of aminoacylation of tRNA was measured by the isolation of ^{14}C-labeled leucyl-tRNA (Ilan, 1969b; Ilan *et al.,* 1970). Figure 3a depicts the kinetics of the formation of ^{14}C-labeled leucyl-tRNA using tRNA and enzyme from day 1. The reaction is linear for about 10 minutes and then proceeds at a decreasing rate. A steady state is reached at about 30 minutes. At 45 minutes (arrow) more tRNA was added and resulted in a second increase in leucyl-tRNA formation, indicating that at the plateau the limiting factor is the availability of tRNA[Leu] while other components, such as ATP and leucine, are present in excess and are available. Moreover, the decreased rate of aminoacylation with time and the plateau level, are not due to inactivation of enzyme under the *in vitro* conditions. Once the kinetics of the reaction were established, the influence of varying the source of either tRNA or enzyme

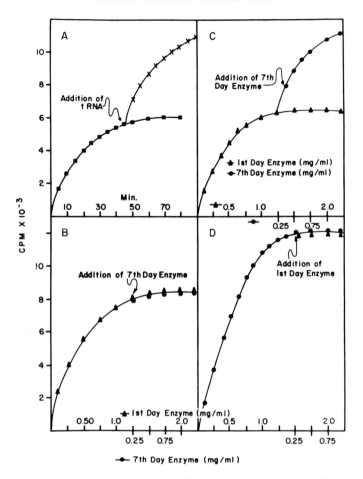

Fig. 3. Changes in leucine acceptor ability during metamorphosis. The formation of ^{14}C-labeled leucyl-tRNA, unless otherwise stated, was carried out at 30°C for 30 minutes. Microsomal wash served as enzyme. (A, B) Day 1 tRNA; (C, D) day 7 tRNA. From Ilan *et al.* (1970).

or both on the formation of leucyl-tRNA was measured. The reaction was stopped after 30 minutes when the rate of aminoacylation had achieved a steady-state level.

The influence of increasing amounts of leucyl-tRNA synthetase on the formation of leucyl-tRNA is shown in Figs. 3b, 3c, and 3d. In all cases, there is a linear increase of leucine esterification, and saturation of enzyme is reached at about 1 mg/ml. Figure 3c shows experiments in which tRNA from day 7 was used as a substrate and was aminoacyl-ated to saturation with increasing amounts of enzyme from day 1. After the saturation point of day 1 enzyme, addition of increasing amounts of enzyme from day 7 resulted in more aminoacylation. These results suggest that leucyl-tRNA synthetase prepared from day 7 animals can recognize more or different subspecies of tRNA^{Leu}. This new leucine acceptor tRNA is not found in tRNA prepared from day 1 pupae (Fig. 3b). In contrast to the experiments shown in Fig. 3c, Fig. 3d shows experiments using tRNA from day 7 which had been aminoacylated to the point of saturation with increasing amounts of enzyme from day 7. Addition of the enzyme fraction from day 1 did not result in increased charging. This suggests that the day 7 enzyme preparation also contains the enzyme present in day 1 preparations. Alternatively, the day 7 enzyme could have all the specificities of day 1 enzyme as well as its additional functions.

Additional evidence for the appearance of a new isoacceptor tRNA^{Leu} during development was obtained from experiments based on the following rationale. If cells from day 7 animals contain an additional isoaccepting tRNA^{Leu} which is discriminately recognized by synthetases, this tRNA may contain a unique sequence of nucleotides if it has originated from different genes. The first guanosine base in the nucleotide sequence starting from the terminal CCA might not be in the same position in the day 7 tRNA^{Leu} as in the day 1 tRNA^{Leu}. This idea was tested in the following way: First day tRNA was isolated and aminoacylated with leucine-^{3}H and day 7 tRNA with leucine-^{14}C. The mixture was digested to completion with T1 ribonuclease in a slightly acidic environment in which the ester bond between the amino acid and the tRNA is stable. The digestion resulted in oligonucleotides with labeled amino acid attached to the 3' terminal. Thus terminal aminoacyl oligonucleotides from day 1 and from day 7 could be compared for differences in length. T1 ribonuclease hydrolyzes at the guanosine-phosphate bond exclusively. Figure 4 shows oligonucleotides that were fractionated according to their length on a column of DEAE-cellulose. The position of the oligonucleotide in the elution gradient at pH 5.5 is largely a function of the number of phosphorus atoms in the fragment. Under these conditions, the ester bond is stable and the terminal oligonucleotide fragment possesses the radioactive amino acid and is thus identified (Ilan et al., 1972).

It is seen from Fig. 4 that tRNA from day 1 animals contains 5 different oligonucleotides which represent the 3' end with the leucine-^{3}H still attached. Day 7 tRNA^{Leu}, when charged with leucine-^{14}C using enzymes from day 7, contained all 5 fragments observed for day 1 tRNA^{Leu} as well as a pronounced new terminal fragment of leucyl-^{14}C-oligonucleotide (Fig. 4, arrow). This additional fragment resulted from tRNA^{Leu} which may be genetically different from that obtained from day 1 tRNA^{Leu}. The distance between the leucine and the first guanosine residue is not the same as that observed for day 1 tRNA^{Leu}. Alternatively,

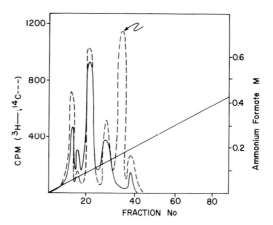

FIG. 4. Chromatography of T1 RNase digestion products of leucyl-tRNA. tRNA preparations from day 7 were charged with leucine-¹⁴C and tRNA from day 1 with leucine-³H as described in Fig. 2. The isolated aminoacyl tRNAs were deproteinized and then mixed and 500 μg of the mixture digested with 500 units of T1 RNase at 37° for 45 minutes in 2 mM EDTA in sodium acetate buffer pH 5.5. The digest was applied to a 1 cm × 5 cm column of DEAE-cellulose and eluted at 4° using a linear gradient of ammonium formate at pH 5.5 in the presence of 7 M urea. CPM: ——, ³H; ---, ¹⁴C. From Ilan et al. (1972).

it may be due to an incomplete digestion resulting from a modified guanylate bond which becomes resistant to T1 ribonuclease digestion. For instance, it is known that the guanylate bond of N^7-methyl G is resistant to T1 ribonuclease digestion. Methylation of tRNA occurs at the macromolecular level. This problem is under investigation, and we now have evidence that there are neither guanosine nor altered guanosine residues in the fragments.

The genetic code specifies six codons for leucine. This implies six tRNA^{Leu} which differ at least in the anticodon sequence of nucleotides. It remains to be shown that the new tRNA^{Leu} from the day 7 which differs at the 3′ end from that of day 1 tRNA^{Leu} varies also in the anticodon sequence.

G. RATES OF CHAIN ELONGATION AND TRANSLATIONAL EFFICIENCY

Most examples brought to show differences in gene activity imply that genes are "turned on" or "turned off." In liver cells the gene for albumin is "turned on" as though genes existed in only two alternative states, active and inactive. However, there is evidence that the same gene can be active to varying degrees. Isozymes of lactic dehydrogenase are an example.

The rate of peptide chain elongation is the number of amino acids in a given protein, divided by its translation time. The translation time is usually measured by the method of Fan and Penman (1970). On the average, once the precursor pool for specific activity has been stabilized *in vivo* the time required for one set of nascent labeled chains to be released is equal to one half the average translation time $(t_{1/2})$. This is so because the nascent peptide chains can be assumed to be half finished.

When such a calculation of translation time is carried out with the whole cell, it is assumed that the average time needed to add a single amino acid to a growing polypeptide chain is similar for all proteins. Therefore, translation efficiency of template mRNA utilization is the same for all mRNA. This also implies that for every mRNA utilized for protein synthesis the template is copied by ribosomes moving along the template (polysomes). That is, the template is copied by multiple copying units, and the overall efficiency of the process is determined by the packing of the ribosomes on the mRNA and by the speed at which they move down along the template. Ribosomes are generally believed to be spaced 30 codons apart along the mRNA, and if they move at the rate of 60 codons per minute the efficiency of translation will be 60/30 = 2 protein chains per mRNA per minute. This is irrespective of the length of mRNA, for a single ribosome requires more time to translate a longer message, but more ribosomes can be packed on a longer message and thus the overall efficiency is the same.

The above-calculated translation time is an average for all mRNA and implies that the time needed to add a single amino acid is always the same for all proteins. To validate such an assumption, the translation time of a single protein should be measured. Moreover, even in a single protein the rate of translation need not be the same. One can imagine that ribosomes moving along the message may slow down at a certain point. This could happen when the ribosomes reach a codon for which the corresponding tRNA is rate limiting. An example is given from the analysis of the incorporation of leucine into different positions of the rabbit globin chain (Dintzis, 1961). Early portions of the alpha chain are assembled rapidly while the portions near the carboxyl terminal are assembled more slowly. A rate-limiting step in the elongation of hemoglobin was also observed with human reticulocytes (Winslow and Ingram, 1966).

Evidence proving that the rate of translation of specific natural mRNA can be differentially slowed or accelerated *in vitro* by simple deletion or addition of tRNA fraction has been provided using a cell-free system from *Tenebrio* (Ilan, 1969b; Ilan *et al.*, 1970, 1972). *Tenebrio* ribosomes from pharate adults (pupae which are completing their development into adults) contain endogenous mRNA for cuticular protein that can synthesize this protein when tRNA and the enzyme fraction is used from animals 7 days after the larval pupal molt, but not with tRNA from day 1. Cuticular protein synthesis in a cell-free system can be identified by the chromatographic analysis of the tryptic digest and its comparison to *in vivo* synthesized cuticle. In contrast, day 1 tRNA supports the synthesis of protein which has a different chromatographic pattern to that of cuticular protein. Under such conditions the ratio of tyrosine to leucine incorporation is low, whereas under conditions in which cuticular protein is synthesized, a high ratio of tyrosine to leucine incorporation is apparent. Therefore, these ratios can serve as an indicator for the type of protein synthesized.

Experiments were designed in which ribosomes from day 7 animals were incubated with limiting amounts of enzyme isolated from animals of the same age. A constant amount of tRNA from day 7 animals was present and varying amounts of tRNA from day 1 were added to the reaction mixture. In a second set of experiments a constnat amount of tRNA from day 1 was present while varying the amount from day 7 animals. These experiments are summarized in Table VIII. It was important that the constant amount that was utilized, as shown in the table,

TABLE VIII

EFFECT OF COMBINING DIFFERENT CONCENTRATIONS OF tRNA
FROM NORMAL AND HORMONE-TREATED ANIMALS
ON AMINO ACID INCORPORATION[a]

Addition of tRNA isolated from day 7 pupae		Incorporation	
Hormone-treated animal (mg) (or day 1 + RNA)	Normal (mg)	Tyrosine (cpm/mg RNA)	Leucine (cpm/mg RNA)
1.0	—	2,300	10,500
0.5	—	2,600	11,800
0.5	0.5	5,400	10,600
0.5	1.0	12,600	9,500
—	1.0	18,400	11,400
—	0.5	18,300	10,600
0.5	0.5	5,900	11,400
1.0	0.5	2,800	10,100
0.5	1.0[b]	2,300	10,800
1.0[b]	0.5	18,000	11,400

[a] From Ilan *et al.* (1970).
[b] Treated with rat liver tRNA-CMP-AMP-pyrophosphorylase.

either for tRNA from day 1 or for tRNA from day 7 was a saturating amount. This is shown in the table. tRNA from day 1 at a level of 0.5 mg was saturating since addition of 1 mg of tRNA from day 1 did not affect the incorporation of either leucine or tyrosine into polypeptide. The same is true for tRNA for day 7. On the other hand, when saturating amounts of tRNA from day 1 are present and tRNA from day 7 was also added in increasing amounts it can be seen (Table VIII) that the ratio of incorporation of tyrosine to leucine was proportional to the amount of 7 day tRNA added above the saturating amount present from day 1. Conversely, when a constant amount of tRNA from day 7 was present at a saturating level and increasing amounts of tRNA from day 1 was added, a decrease in the ratio of tyrosine to leucine was obtained. This decrease is proportional the amount of day 1 tRNA added above the saturating level of day 7 tRNA. In all experiments described in Table VIII, the enzyme was taken from day 7. As we have seen before, this enzyme is capable of recognizing tRNA from both sources. We also know that changes in ratios of incorporation are changes in the type of protein synthesized. Therefore, the gradual change in ratios with the addition of a new source of tRNA after saturation with the first source clearly indicates different rates of translation of individual mRNAs regulated by a rate-limiting rare species of tRNA.

This observation is not unique for insect development. Anderson (1969) suggested that AGA and AGG both might be arginine regulatory codons in bacteria. He showed that the rate of polypeptide synthesis was stimulated in direct proportion to the addition of arginine tRNA corresponding to AGA and AGG when poly(AG) was used as a message, indicating a rate-limiting amount of arginine tRNA. It follows that any change in the abundance of the individual tRNA species would be potentially capable of changing the rate of mRNA translation. Using a rabbit reticulocyte cell-free system capable of synthesizing hemoglobin, Weisblum et al. (1965) demonstrated that two separate fractions insert leucine into different positions in the hemoglobin chain. Since different species of tRNA can be responsible for inserting the same amino acid into the hemoglobin chain, the presence of limiting amounts of one species might produce a reduced rate of mRNA translation at a given point. Indeed, such evidence was presented recently by showing unequal chain synthesis of chains of hemoglobin in vitro (Anderson and Gilbert, 1969). This was regulated by the source of tRNA. It was concluded that even though the alpha and beta chains both contain all 20 amino acids, the alpha chain must contain at least one codon which is used either less often or not at all in beta chain synthesis. It has recently been shown that the rate of peptide chain elongation in a uterus cell-free system is increased after administration of estradiol (Whelly and Barker, 1974). Moreover, changes in the rate of mRNA translation *in vivo* in the ovalbumin system have been reported recently (Schimke *et al.*, 1973).

From the *Tenebrio*, the bacterial, and the mammalian systems, we have seen that the appearance of the final gene product, the protein, can be regulated by the rates of mRNA translation. This may be one reason for the apparent differences in gene activity. Therefore, a gradual increase in an enzyme protein or a structural protein during development need not necessarily mean a gradual increase in the rate of gene transcription, but may also be a gradual increase in the rate of mRNA translation.

H. EVIDENCE THAT tRNA REGULATES AT THE LEVEL OF CHAIN ELONGATION

We have shown that tRNA is involved in translational control of protein synthesis. tRNA from early stages of development differs from that of later stages. In addition, juvenile hormone promotes changes in late tRNA. tRNA from the various sources mentioned affects discrimination as to which mRNA is to be translated. tRNA is involved in the translational machinery in at least three points: at peptide chain initiation, at peptide chain elongation, and at the termination of the polypeptide chain. Regulation may occur at each of these levels. Therefore, it was important to determine the point of regulation. First, we examined the capacity of the system to initiate polypeptide chain synthesis. Table IX shows that when microsomal preparations are incubated with ^{14}C-labeled algal hydrolyzate and the incorporation of ^{14}C-labeled amino acids into NH_2-terminal position is measured, 5–10% of the labeled amino acids are in the NH_2-terminal position. Conversely, on purified ribosomes no incorporation into NH_2-position was observed.

It is possible that the lack of NH_2-terminal labeling on purified ribosomes might be a result of a blocked amino group at the NH_2-terminal position of the polypeptide chain. However, it seems more likely that the purified ribosomes have lost chain-initiation factors, since the purification involves three washings in 0.5 M KCl (Ilan, 1968). Such a procedure is known to remove initiation factors from bacterial ribosomes. Moreover, reticulocyte ribosomes purified in the same manner lost their ability to incorporate valine-^{14}C into the NH_2-terminal position of hemoglobin (Bishop, 1966).

Next, we looked for chain termination on purified ribosomes. We had previously observed that a crude microsomal system is capable of releasing about 30% of the labeled protein (Ilan *et al.*, 1970; Ilan, 1973). However, chain termination does not occur in the purified ribosomal system.

TABLE IX

CHAIN INITIATION IN CELL-FREE SYSTEM[a,b]

Expt. No.	Conditions	Incorporation	
		NH₂-terminal (cpm/mg protein)	Internal (cpm/mg protein)
1	Microsomes	516	5974
2	Microsomes	354	5863
3	Ribosomes	0	7956
4	Ribosomes	0	8211

[a] From Ilan et al. (1970).

[b] Incubation conditions were as described in Table IV, except that ¹⁴C-labeled algal hydrolyzate was used, and in some experiments microsomes were used. The hot trichloroacetic acid precipitate was washed with ether. The protein (3 mg per sample) was suspended in 3 ml of H_2O in excess of fluorodinitrobenzene for 80 minutes at pH 9 and 40°. The pH was maintained by addition of 2 N NaOH. Excess of fluoro-dinitrobenzene was extracted with ether and the solution was acidified to 6 N HCl and hydrolyzed for 16 hours at 100°C. The precipitated 2,4-dinitrophenyl derivatives were separated by centrifugation, resuspended in ether, and aliquots were counted. Portions from the supernatant fluid of the 2,4-dinitrophenyl derivatives served for measurement of internal peptide labeling. The recovery of radioactivity was close to 70%.

This is evident from the following experiment: when a complete reaction mixture was cooled after 5 minutes of incubation and analyzed by sucrose gradient sedimentation most of the protein that was synthesized in the cell-free system is in the polysome region.

The same analysis was applied to a sample after 30 minutes of incubation. From previous kinetic studies it was known that the reaction is over after 30 minutes (Ilan, 1968). The polysomes had broken down to monosomes. However, the newly synthesized protein was not released from the monosomes (Fig. 5). Therefore, the involvement of tRNA in regulation of mRNA translation is not at the chain-termination level. The only remaining possibility for involvement of tRNA in mRNA translation is in regulation at the chain elongation level.

V. Experiments on Initiation of mRNA Translation during Development of *Tenebrio*

It is believed that in eukaryotic organisms protein synthesis is initiated in a manner similar to bacterial protein synthesis. First, it was shown in protozoa (Ilan, 1969c; Ilan and Ilan, 1970) and later in ascites tumor cells (Smith and Marcker, 1970; Brown and Smith, 1970) that

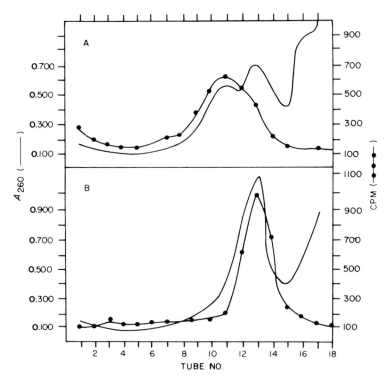

Fig. 5. Localization of newly synthesized polypeptide during incubation of purified ribosomes. Incubations were carried out as described in the legend to Table IV, except for the time. After incubation [(A) 5 minutes; (B) 30 minutes], the tubes were placed in ice and their contents were layered on a 10 to 40% sucrose gradient (4.5 ml). After centrifugation for 90 minutes at 39,000 rpm, drops were collected from the bottom (2 drops per sample), diluted to 1 ml for optical density determination, after which 5 ml of 5% trichloroacetic acid were added and the samples were heated for 20 minutes at 90°. The protein was collected and washed on Millipore filters and counted. From Ilan *et al.* (1970).

in a cell-free system containing all tRNAs, only synthetic mRNAs with the methionine codon AUG at or near the 5′-end are translated at low Mg^{2+} concentration. Eukaryotic cells contain two species of methionyl-tRNA (Brown and Smith, 1970; Caskey *et al.*, 1967; Takeishi *et al.*, 1968). One tRNA inserts methionine only into the NH_2-terminal position and is known as $tRNA_f^{Met}$ since it can be formylated by bacterial transformylase. However, cytoplasmic sap from eukaryotic organisms does not contain transformylase. The second $tRNA_m^{Met}$ inserts methionine only internally in the growing peptide chain. Both species of tRNA are readily isolated using benzoated-DEAE cellulose columns. Not only synthetic mRNA but a few natural mRNAs from eukaryotic cells have been shown to initiate with methionine. This was shown recently for the alpha and beta chain of globin (Jackson and Hunter, 1970; Wilson and Dintzis, 1970; Housman *et al.*, 1970) and for the protamine in trout testes cells (Wigle and Dixon, 1970). The fact that the majority of completed proteins in eukaryotic organisms do not contain methionine at the N-terminal position is best explained by the finding that the N-terminal methionyl residue is removed by the action of an amino peptidase at an early stage of chain elongation (Bhaduri *et al.*, 1970; Housman *et al.*, 1970; Yoshida *et al.*, 1970; Kerwar *et al.*, 1971).

A. REQUIREMENTS FOR THE FORMATION OF A COMPLETE 80 S INITIATION COMPLEX IN *Tenebrio*

In prokaryotes, for protein synthesis to start, mRNA binds to the small (30 S) ribosomal subunit and the initiator formylmethionine tRNA connects to its AUG codon. Concomitantly the large ribosomal subunit (50 S) joins the 30 S to form a 70 S complete initiation complex. Three initiation factors function in the formation of the initiation complex. They can be isolated from ribosomes by extraction with 1 M ammonium chloride or potassium chloride. GTP is also needed to promote the binding of bacterial initiator fMet-tRNA to the initiation complex. It appears that during initiation of protein synthesis in bacteria, a monosome (70 S unit) is formed by association of free small and large ribosomal subunits arising from ribosomes which were dissociated after chain termination (Lipmann, 1969). For eukaryotes there is no such wealth of available information. However, studies involving the ribosomal–polysomal cycle in mammalian systems and studies on the formation of the initiation complex suggest that this model for protein synthesis may also apply (Kaempfer, 1969; Hogan and Korner, 1968; Kabat and Rich, 1969; Joklik and Becker, 1965). Moreover, it was recently shown that three factors are required for initiation of the synthesis of new and complete hemoglobin alpha and beta chains at low Mg^{2+} concentration (Prichard *et al.*, 1970). An illustration summarizing initiation of mRNA translation is shown in Fig. 6. In this figure the small ribosomal subunit appears as 40 S, the large ribosomal subunit as 60 S, and the associated monosome, which represents the complete initiation complex including mRNA and Met-tRNA, is 80 S. These sedimentation values are usual for eukaryotic ribosomes and their subunits.

A study on the formation of complete 80 S initiation complex in *Tenebrio* has appeared recently (Ilan and Ilan, 1971). The components of the *in vitro* system consisted of 40 S ribosomal subunits, 60 S ribosomal subunits, labeled ribonucleoprotein as mRNA source, GTP, amino-

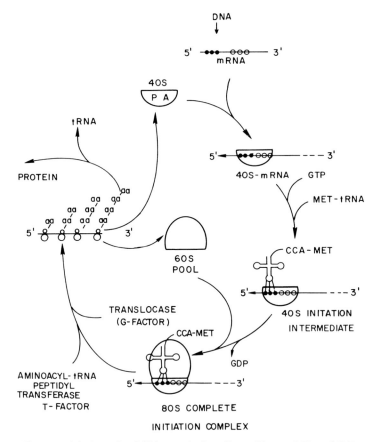

FIG. 6. Initiation of mRNA translation. From Ilan and Ilan (1971).

acyl tRNA, and crude initiation factors. The formation of 80 S initiation complex was determined by sucrose gradient analysis in which an 80 S component was formed and could be identified spectrophotometrically. The labeled mRNA moved with the 80 S initiation complex. For these studies the components of the initiation complex were prepared in the following way. Insects were labeled *in vivo* for 30 minutes with uridine-[14]C. This time period was chosen since previous experiments had shown that no significant label was detected as ribosomal RNA before 45 minutes of exposure to the radioisotopes. Polysomes were prepared, and they are shown in Fig. 7a. Most of the label from uridine is in the polysomal region. These polysomes were treated with 1 *M* KCl. This treatment dissociated the ribosomes from the polysomes and from the monosome peak into ribosomal subunits and released the mRNA as ribo-

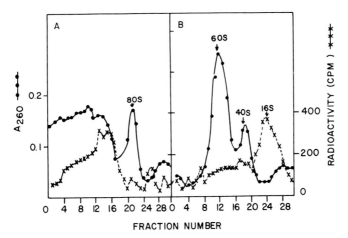

FIG. 7. Release of messenger ribonucleoprotein from polysomes. Seventh-day pupae were labeled for 30 minutes with uridine-^{14}C. Polysomes were prepared as described by Ilan and Ilan (1971). They were divided into two parts. One (A) was layered on a 10 to 40% sucrose gradient in buffer A and centrifuged for 90 minutes at 39,000 rpm in an SW 65 rotor at 4°C. Drops were collected from the bottom and analyzed for optical density and radioactivity. Another portion (B) was suspended in buffer containing 12 mM MgCl$_2$, 1 M KCl, 10 mM DTT, and 5 μg/ml of polyvinyl sulfate. The suspension was layered onto 4.5 ml of 15 to 30% sucrose containing the same buffer and centrifuged for 3 hours at 28°C in the same rotor and speed as (A). From Ilan and Ilan (1971).

nucleoprotein particle (mRNP) in a polydisperse array between 100 and 16 S with a pronounced peak of radioactivity at 16 S. The 16 S RNP peak with labeled RNA (Fig. 7B) served as mRNA source for studies on the formation of the initiation complex. Phenol extraction of the RNA from the 16 S RNP gave a peak value of 10 S RNA. Initiation factors were prepared from monosomes obtained from crude polysomes omitting the KCl wash (Ilan, 1968). These polysomes were incubated in a complete system for protein synthesis for 30 minutes at 30 degrees. This treatment was shown to break the polysomes completely to monosomes (Ilan et al., 1970) presumably because of degradation of mRNA (Ilan, 1973). Initiation factors were extracted from these monosomes with 1 M KCl.

Formation of the initiation complex was detected by determination of the position of the radioactivity on sucrose gradient as well as by detecting the 80 S peak spectrophotometrically. This is illustrated in Fig. 8A. This figure shows sedimentation analysis of the complete system which includes ^{14}C-labeled RNP as mRNA, 40 S ribosomal subunits, 60 S ribosomal subunits, initiation factors, GTP, and aminoacyl tRNA acylated with all 20 amino acids. Most of the radioactivity was associated

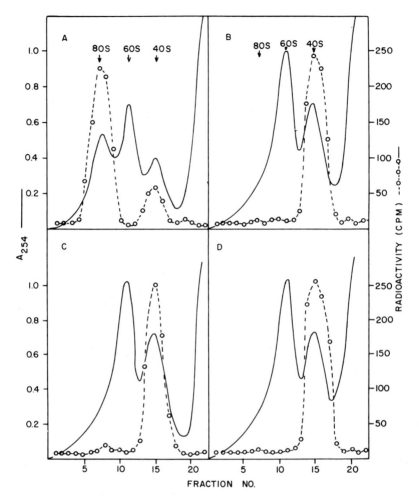

Fig. 8. Requirements for the formation of the complete initiation complex. The complete mixture was contained in 0.5 ml and incubated for 10 minutes at 30°C. It consisted of 50 mM Tris-HCl (pH 7.6), 6 mM MgCl$_2$, 50 mM KCl, 10 mM DTT, 0.5 mg of ribosomal subunits (an equal mixture of 60 S and 40 S), 0.5 mM GTP, 0.5 mg aminoacyl-tRNA, 200 μg of initiation protein, and 1000 cpm of RNP as mRNA. After incubation, the tubes were rapidly cooled and layered on 15 to 30% sucrose gradient in buffer A. The mixture was centrifuged for 1 hour at 60,000 rpm in an SW rotor at 4°C. Optical density was recorded automatically, and drops were collected for determination of radioactivity. (A) The complete system; (B) less GTP; (C) less protein initiation factor; (D) deacylated-tRNA replaced aminoacyl-tRNA. From Ilan and Ilan (1971).

with the 80 S ribosomes. It is also clear that there is a strict requirement for the formation of the complete 80 S initiation complex. When GTP (Fig. 8B) or initiation factors (Fig. 8C) were omitted, or when aminoacyl-tRNA was replaced with deacylated tRNA, no 80 S initiation complex was formed.

B. SPECIFICITY OF CHAIN INITIATION DURING DEVELOPMENT

Studies with bacteria showed that ribosomes do not recognize identically all cistrons of mRNA. Lodish (1969), by comparing ribosomes from different bacterial species, demonstrated that ribosomes differentiate the three cistrons of f2 RNA. It was also shown (Hsu and Weiss, 1969) that after infection with T4 bacteriophage, *E. coli* ribosomes translate T4 mRNA much more efficiently than f2 RNA. Therefore, this experiment suggests that mRNA contains, besides AUG, a specific signal that is recognized by some element of the initiation machinery. *E. coli* has three initiation factors F1, F2, and F3. Initiation factor F3 plays a role in recognition of this signal (Revel *et al.*, 1970). Moreover, modification of template specificity after T4 bacteriophage infection, which leads to preferential initiation of late T4 mRNA translation, can be accounted for by change in initiation factor F3 activity. In other words, bacterial ribosomes are specific for mRNA binding. That is, a template-specific initiation reaction is taking place, by which ribosomes can recognize selectively the proper mRNA to be translated. This may provide a mechanism of gene expression controlled at the level of translation.

With *Tenebrio* it was shown that there is a stage-specific initiation factor which promotes the formation of the 80 S complete initiation complex only with mRNA extracted from the same stage of development as (mRNP). This is shown in Fig. 9. The formation of the complete 80 S initiation complex occurs when all added components belong to the same stage of development (Fig. 9A). However, when ¹⁴C-labeled mRNA is taken from pharate adults and initiation factors from larvae, no initiation complex was formed (Fig. 9B). Similar results were obtained when mRNA-¹⁴C was from larvae and initiation factor was from pharate adult. Again no initiation complex was formed (Fig. 9C). On the other hand, when both mRNA and initiation factors from larvae were used, a complete 80 S initiation complex was formed (Fig. 9D). These results indicate the existence of stage-specific initiation factors (Ilan and Ilan, 1971). The source of the ribosomes was not important in obtaining these sets of results.

Two possible interpretations may be found for the results presented above: (1) A group of mRNAs from a given stage of development may have a specific sequence of oligonucleotides preceding the AUG codon

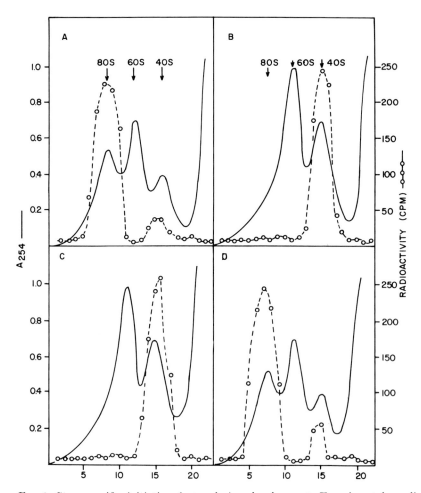

Fig. 9. Stage-specific initiation factor during development. Experimental conditions used were as described in the legend for Fig. 8. In all cases, day 7 pupae ribosomal subunits were used. RNP was used as mRNA, and initiation protein factors were prepared from last-instar larvae or 7-day pupae and used in combinations as described above. (A) Pupal mRNA and pupal initiation factors; (B) pupal mRNA and larval initiation factor; (C) larval mRNA and pupal initiation factor; (D) larval mRNA and larval initiation factors. From Ilan and Ilan (1971).

recognized by a unique initiation factor. Such a sequence is known for viral mRNA. Protein synthesis directed by viral RNA does not begin immediately at the 5' end of phage RNA because the sequence of the first few nucleotides in viral chains do not contain one of the fMet codons AUG or GUG necessary for initiating phage protein synthesis

(DeWachter *et al.*, 1968; DeWachter and Fiers, 1969; Adams and Cory, 1970; Steitz, 1969). Moreover, recently the nucleotide sequence of the three ribosomal binding sites in R17 phage RNA was described (Steitz, 1969). These untranslated sequences extend many nucleotides on the 5' end of each of the initiation codons for three R17 proteins, namely, the phage coat protein, the A protein, and R17 RNA replicase. (2) The secondary structure of mRNA may be stage specific and thus recognized by a unique initiation factor on the ribosomes. Here again, such a possibility was shown in the regulation of initiation of translation of three f2 phage proteins by phage RNA. When the secondary structure of the RNA was partially disrupted by mild reaction with formaldehyde the ability of the RNA to direct synthesis of both RNA polymerase and maturation protein increases up to 20-fold (Lodish, 1970). No experimental evidence is available to support either of the possibilities in the *Tenebrio* system.

Finally, the above observation may explain the stimulation in ribosome synthesis by almost all hormones studied. It may be that new ribosomes containing new initiation factor are needed to facilitate translation of hormone-specific mRNA. If this is true, a qualitative change in at least one of the ribosomal proteins should be noted. We have observed such a change on insect ribosomes after treatment with ecdysone (J. Ilan and J. Ilan, unpublished observation).

C. ISOLATION AND IDENTIFICATION OF THREE INITIATION FACTORS

The experiments on the formation of the 80 S initiation complex indicated developmental specificity of the initiation factors. Crude factors were used. However, in order to elucidate the mechanism, the individual factors involved in initiation had to be identified and characterized.

The first indication of the involvement of initiation factors in the initiation of mRNA translation in insects was obtained from studies in cell-free system of *Tenebrio* (Ilan *et al.*, 1970). When microsome preparations were incubated with ^{14}C-labeled algal hydrolyzate and the incorporation of the ^{14}C-labeled amino acids into the NH_2-terminal position was measured, 5–10% of the labeled amino acids were incorporated in the NH_2-terminal position. This was measured by modifying the NH_2-terminal amino acid of the proteins into dinitrophenyl derivatives. After acid hydrolysis the dinitrophenyl-^{14}C amino acids are precipitated while amino acid incorporated into internal positions of the peptide were solubilized. Conversely, purified ribosomes did not incorporate amino acids into the NH_2-terminal position, but only into internal positions of the polypeptide chain. This is illustrated in Table IX. Here is the first indication that purified ribosomes from insects lost chain initiation factors. This was not surprising since purification involves washing ribosomes in 0.5 M KCl (Ilan, 1968). Such a procedure is known to remove initiation factors from bacterial and mammalian ribosomes. It also points to the fact that high salt wash removes initiation factors.

Three factors that control the initiation of mRNA translation have been identified. They are involved in binding and positioning of the AUG region of mRNA on ribosomes and in recognition of initiator tRNA. Such initiation factors have been reported for both bacterial and mammalian systems (Lengyel and Söll, 1969).

In *Tenebrio* three factors are also required for the initiation of mRNA translation. Two of the factors, I_1 and I_2, are able to initiate translation of the synthetic messenger $AUG(U)_n$ at low Mg^{2+} concentration. However, three factors, I_1, I_2, and I_3, are necessary for the translation of natural mRNA. Factor I_3 was isolated from mRNA when the latter was released from polysomes as ribonucleoprotein complex (Ilan and Ilan, 1973c).

As a first approach to reactions leading to initiation of mRNA translation in insect preparations. $AUG(U)_n$ was used. AUG calls for methionine whereas poly(U) calls for polyphenylalanine. In a cell-free system containing all tRNAs, only synthetic mRNA with the methionine AUG codon at its 5' end was translated at low Mg^{2+} concentration (Ilan and Ilan, 1970). Under these conditions methionine is incorporated at the N-terminal of polyphenylalanine. At low Mg^{2+} the initiation factors discriminate binding of Met-tRNA to the AUG codon (Ilan and Ilan, 1970).

Factors I_1 and I_2 were separated from monosomes. Factor I_3 was obtained from the mRNA–protein complexes. Monosomes were obtained by treatment of polysomes with puromycin (50 $\mu g/ml$) followed by centrifugation in an SW 65 rotor for 90 minutes at 50,000 rpm in a 10 to 40% sucrose gradient.

Puromycin treatment of polysomes released peptidyl-tRNA and mRNA-protein complex. The resultant monosomes obtained from the 80 S peak (runoff ribosomes) were washed in 1 M KCl. The wash served as a source of I_1 and I_2. Alternatively, crude initiation factors were prepared from monosomes obtained from polysomes which had been incubated in a complete system for protein synthesis for 30 minutes at 30° (preincubated ribosomes). This treatment was shown to break the polysomes to monosomes. However, mRNA was not released, as evident from lack of chain termination and the association of peptidyl-tRNA with the 80 S monosome peak (Ilan *et al.*, 1970; Ilan, 1973).

Initiation factors I_1 and I_2 were obtained as ribosomal wash from runoff ribosomes and separated on Sephadex G-200. They were identified

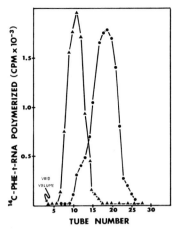

Fig. 10. Separation of I_1 (●——●) and I_2 (▲——▲) by Sephadex G-200 chromatography. Puromycin treated runoff ribosomes from 100 gm of day 1 pupae of *Tenebrio* were used. They were washed with 1 M KCl, and the crude initiation factors were obtained from the ribosomal wash as previously described; 2 ml of ribosomal wash containing 20 mg of protein was placed on a 0.9×50 cm Sephadex G-200 column, equilibrated with buffer containing 0.1 M KCl, 3 mM Tris-HCl, pH 7.5, 1 mM dithiothreitol, and 0.05 M K⁺-EDTA at 23°C. Fractions of 1 ml were collected at a flow rate of 10 ml per hour. Activities of I_1 and I_2 were determined by AUG(U)$_n$-directed polyphenylalanine at low Mg^{2+} concentration, as previously described (Ilan and Ilan, 1970) in the presence of protein as polymerization enzymes (containing the elongation factors T and G) and ribosomes washed in 1 M KCl. For activity of I_1, a 0.1-ml aliquot from each fraction was added in the presence of 200 μg of I_2 (tube No. 10). For activity of I_2 a constant amount of 200 μg I_1 (tube No. 20) was present; 0.1 ml from each tube was added. From Ilan and Ilan (1973c).

by their ability to stimulate polyphenylalanine synthesis directed by AUG(U)$_n$ at low Mg^{2+}. The system also included elongation factors. Figure 10 shows that on Sephadex G-200 I_1 and I_2 could be separated almost completely. Although I_1 and I_2 functioned very efficiently with AUG(U)$_n$, they failed to initiate protein synthesis directed by natural mRNA as judged by the incorporation of leucine into hot TCA precipitate; 10 S RNA stripped from polysomes served as natural mRNA.

Factors I_1 and I_2 used in these experiments had been prepared from puromycin-treated runoff monosomes devoid of mRNA. Neither the isolated factors nor the crude 1 M KCl ribosomal wash from runoff ribosomes was able to stimulate polypeptide chain initiation directed by natural mRNA. In contrast, ribosomal wash obtained from regular monosomes possessing endogenous mRNA could initiate polypeptide chain synthesis directed by exogenously supplied natural mRNA. Gel filtration of ribosomal wash obtained from preincubated ribosomes resulted in two peaks similar to those shown in Fig. 10. However, addition of these two peaks brought about the initiation of polypeptide chain synthesis directed by natural mRNA. Therefore, ribosomes possessing mRNA contain an additional factor required for the initiation of natural mRNA translation. The third factor does not separate from either I_1 or I_2 under these conditions.

For preparation of I_3, polysomes were obtained and mRNA was separated as ribonucleoprotein particles by treatment with 1 M KCl. Protein was separated from the mRNA–protein complex and was chromatographed on a Sephadex G-200 column. This protein eluted at the same position as I_2 (Fig. 11). Factor I_3 is functionally different from I_2 as

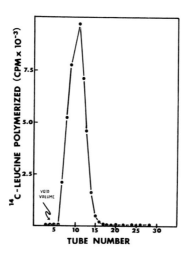

Fig. 11. Fractionation of I_3 by Sephadex G-200. Factor I_3 was extracted from the 16 S mRNA–protein complex released from polysomes with 1 M KCl. Two milliliters containing 20 mg of protein was placed on Sephadex G-200. Fractionation and determination of I_3 were as described for I_1 and I_2 in Fig. 10 except that each test tube contained 0.2 mg of I_1, as well as of I_2, 100 μg of 10 S natural mRNA (replacing AUG(U)$_n$) and 0.01 mg of tRNA charged with leucine-^{14}C (15,000 cpm) and 19 ^{12}C-amino acids. From Ilan and Ilan (1973c).

evident from its requirement for initiation of natural mRNA translation. Table X shows the requirement of initiation factors for natural mRNA-directed protein synthesis and for AUG(U)$_n$-directed polyphenylalanine synthesis at low Mg^{2+}. Factors I_1 or I_2 individually had a very limited capacity to initiate polypeptide synthesis by either natural or

TABLE X

REQUIREMENTS FOR NATURAL MESSENGER AND
AUG(U)$_n$-DIRECTED PROTEIN SYNTHESIS[a,b]

| | Incorporation (cpm) | |
| | Leucine-^{14}C protein synthesis directed by | Phe-^{14}C polyphenylalanine synthesis directed |
Additions	natural mRNA	by AUG(U)$_n$
I$_1$	350	150
I$_2$	420	200
I$_3$	0	0
I$_1$ + I$_2$	550	7,500
I$_1$ + I$_3$	400	180
I$_2$ + I$_3$	800	50
I$_1$ + I$_2$ + I$_3$	7,950	7,200
Ribosomal wash (from preincubated ribosomes)	11,300	7,800
Runoff ribosomal wash	480	7,300

[a] From Ilan and Ilan (1973c).

[b] Experimental conditions for polyphenylalanine synthesis directed by AUG(U)$_n$ were as described in Fig. 10. Conditions for incorporation of leucine-^{14}C directed by natural messengers were as in Fig. 11, except for addition of factors that are given above. Each factor when added was at a level of 50 μg. Ribosomal wash was prepared by washing monosomes with 1 M KCl as described in Fig. 10 from preincubated ribosomes possessing endogenous mRNA or from puromycin-treated runoff ribosomes devoid of endogenous mRNA. In both cases, ribosomal wash was added at the level of 0.2 mg of crude protein.

synthetic mRNA. I$_3$ had none. Combination of I$_1$ and I$_2$ was capable of initiating polyphenylalanine synthesis directed by the synthetic mRNA but failed to stimulate polypeptide chain synthesis directed by natural mRNA. Factor I$_1$ together with I$_3$ or I$_2$ together with I$_3$ did not stimulate initiation of polypeptide synthesis directed by either natural or synthetic mRNA. All three factors together stimulate the initiation of mRNA translation directed by either natural mRNA or synthetic mRNA.

It is also evident from Table X that the crude ribosomal wash obtained from puromycin-treated runoff ribosomes is able to initiate only polyphenylalanine synthesis, but not natural mRNA translation. Ribosomal wash obtained from preincubated ribosomes still having mRNA initiates polypeptide chain synthesis directed by either synthetic or natural mRNA. These results indicate that protein attached to mRNA and released from polysomes as RNP has a biological significance. This RNP is not an artifact that resulted from nonspecific association of mRNA with ribosomal protein released under high salt.

These results also indicate that natural mRNA from insects contains, besides AUG, a sequence of nucleotides preceding the AUG codon. This sequence may be recognized by I_3. This is in agreement with the specificity observed for the formation of the 80 S initiation complex in *Tenebrio*.

Further characterization of the three initiation factors is given in Fig. 12. The enzyme concentration curves were determined for I_1 in the pres-

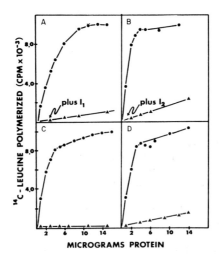

Fig. 12. Natural mRNA directed leucine-^{14}C incorporation into protein as a function of concentration of I_1, I_2, or I_3. Experimental conditions for incorporation were as described in Fig. 11. In each experiment a constant saturating amount of 200 μg of one of the factors was present as well as variable amounts of the other two factors as indicated. (A) I_2 constant; ●——●, plus I_1 and I_3; ▲——▲, plus I_1. (B) I_1 constant; ●——●, plus I_2 and I_3; ▲——▲, plus I_2. (C) I_1 constant; ●——●, plus I_2 and I_3; ▲——▲, plus I_3. (D) I_3 constant; ●——●, plus I_1 and I_2; ▲——▲, plus I_2. From Ilan and Ilan (1973c).

ence of saturating amounts of I_2 and I_3, for I_2 in the presence of saturating amounts of I_1 and I_2. Over a wide concentration range, none of the factors alone produced significant activity. Moreover, a combination of two factors was without effect over a wide concentration range. Only the combination of all three factors, two of which are saturating and one variable, could produce a concentration dependency as expressed in Fig. 12 for the translation of natural mRNA.

D. INVOLVEMENT OF I_2 AND GTP IN THE FORMATION OF 40 S INITIATION COMPLEX

The first reaction leading to the complete initiation complex is the formation of the 40 S initiation complex. The 40 S complex can be measured readily owing to the property of the ribonucleoprotein to adsorb to a nitrocellulose membrane. Table XI shows the involvement of I_2 and GTP in the formation of 40 S initiation complex in *Tenebrio*. $AUG(U)_n$ served as mRNA. Complex formation was dependent on mRNA, Met-tRNA, I_2, and 40 S ribosomal subunits. Table XI shows that under opti-

TABLE XI

INVOLVEMENT OF I_2 IN THE FORMATION OF 40 S INITIATION COMPLEX[a]

	Binding to 40 S subunits (pmoles)[b]			
Additions or omissions	GTP-^{3}H	GTP-γ-^{32}P	Met-tRNA-^{14}C	Phosphate-γ-^{32}P cleaved
Complete	3.3	3.0	3.2	0.1
Less $AUG(U)_n$	0.1	0.2	0.1	0.2
Less Met-tRNA	0.1	0.2	—	0.1
Less I_2	0.2	0.3	0.1	0.2
Less 40 S subunits	0.3	0.2	0.0	0.1
Complete, plus 60 S subunits	0.4	0.3	2.9	3.0

[a] From Ilan and Ilan (1973c).

[b] The reaction mixture contained 0.5 mg of 40 S, 50 pmoles of Met-tRNA, 0.1 mg of $AUG(U)_n$, 50 μg of I_1, 0.5 mM GTP (double labeled with ^{3}H and ^{32}P), 4 mM MgCl$_2$, 150 mM KCl, 50 mM Tris-HCl, pH 7.6, and 1 mM dithiothreitol. The 0.5-ml reaction mixture was incubated for 15 minutes at 30°C; 5 ml of ice cold buffer containing Tris, MgCl$_2$, dithiothreitol, and KCl (at the same concentrations as in the reaction mixture) was then added. The contents of each tube were filtered through Millipore filters and washed four times with 5 ml of the same buffer. Phosphate-γ-^{32}P cleavage was measured in the filtrate.

mal conditions almost equimolar amounts of GTP and Met-tRNA are bound to the 40 S complex, and only negligible amounts of γ-^{32}P splits from GTP-γ-^{32}P. The binding of GTP and met-tRNA to the 40 S complex is completely dependent on I_2. Since these experiments were performed in the presence of saturating amounts of I_1, it is obvious that I_2 functions in the formation of the 40 S complex. Addition of 60 S subunits brought about cleavage of all γ-^{32}P from GTP without release of Met-tRNA from the complex. This may be due to the requirement of energy for binding the 60 S subunit or for the positioning and translocation of the AUG-Met-tRNA to the ribosomal P site.

VI. Sequence Homology at the 5′-Termini of *Tenebrio* mRNA

The specificity in the formation of 80 S initiation complex suggests that mRNA contains, besides the AUG codon for methionine, a specific sequence of nucleotides that is recognized by some elements of the initiation machinery. This signal may involve a sequence that precedes the AUG codon. This idea is supported by the fact that only two initiation factors are needed to initiate protein synthesis directed by synthetic mRNA $AUG(U)_n$, but three are required to initiate the translation of natural mRNA. Therefore, the third initiation factor may function in recognizing a sequence of nucleotides preceding the AUG codon. This possibility prompted us to examine the 5′-terminus of *Tenebrio* polysomal mRNA.

A. Isolation of the 15 Nucleotides at the 5′-Terminus of mRNA

Polysomal mRNA was isolated and treated with alkaline phosphatase to cleave the 5′-phosphates. It was then allowed to react with cyanoethyl-phosphate-^{32}P in pyridine under conditions that favor phosphorylation at the 5′-OH end (Ilan and Ilan, 1973a). 5′-^{32}P-labeled RNA was digested with T1 ribonuclease in the presence of 5.0 mg of yeast RNA. The hydrolyzate was chromatographed on a column of DEAE-cellulose with a sodium chloride linear gradient (0 to 0.4 M), in the presence of 20 mM ammonium formate (pH 5.5) and 7 M urea. Under such conditions the elution of the oligonucleotides is a function of the number of phosphorus atoms in the fragment. All ^{32}P-labeled material was eluted at a position corresponding to 16 phosphorus atoms (Fig. 13), which is that of an oligonucleotide containing 16 nucleotides. However, since the fragment contained an additional phosphate group at the 5′-terminus, we consider it to be of 15 nucleotide residues by identifying peak 5 and counting the subsequent peaks. This fragment may be 14 or 16 nucleotides long, since the elution position from DEAE-cellulose is influenced also by base composition. Addition of 1 M sodium chloride eluted the remaining oligonucleotides from the column as one peak containing about 18 A_{260} units devoid of any radioactivity.

When 5′-^{32}P-labeled mRNA was subjected to alkaline hydrolysis and electrophoresis, a ^{32}P-labeled pAp was identified. This was the only labeled component to appear which indicated that all polysomal mRNAs possess an adenosine residue at the 5′-terminus. Alternatively, it is possible that phosphorylation with cyanoethylphosphate has a specific action confined to oligonucleotides which commence with an A residue. This is

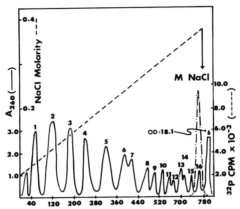

FIG. 13. Chromatography of a T1 ribonuclease digest of mRNA labeled with
[32]P at the 5′-terminus. 10 S mRNA was labeled at the 5′-terminus with ^{32}P by treatment with ^{32}P cyanoethyl phosphate, after treatment with alkaline phosphatase to
release 5′-phosphates. The RNA was digested with T1 ribonuclease in the presence
of 5.0 mg of yeast RNA. The digest was loaded on a column (2 × 100 cm) of
DEAE-cellulose (chloride) and eluted with a gradient of NaCl (0 to 0.4 M) containing 20 mM ammonium formate (pH 5.5) and 7 M urea. The peak on the extreme
rights represents 18.1 A_{260} units and is eluted with 1 M NaCl. From Ilan and Ilan
(1973a).

unlikely, as proved in control experiments with oligonucleotides with
known 5′-terminals such as TMV RNA (5′-A,U,G,C), *E. coli* fMet-
tRNA (5′-C) and *Xenopus* 5 S RNA (5′-G).

B. Sequencing the 5′-Terminus Region

mRNA was labeled *in vivo* with adenosine-[14]C. Previous experiments
had shown that only oligonucleotides eluted from the DEAE-cellulose
column at peaks 1–8 had a significant number of counts when total
mRNA was labeled with adenosine. Thereafter, a radioactive smear was
obtained that was slightly above background counts, except one defined
peak of the 15 nucleotides that was pronounced because it is probably
common to all mRNAs. After isolation of the mRNA, treatment with
phosphodiesterase, and T1 digestion, the 15-nucleotide terminal fragment
was obtained by chromatography on DEAE-cellulose. It was identified
by its position, as determined by chromatography. This fragment was
digested with pancreatic ribonuclease, which cleaves after a pyrimidine.
Therefore, the hydrolyzate could contain only labeled oligonucleotides
composed of A or poly(A) terminating in C or U. A diagram showing
the position of a labeled oligonucleotide from a ribonuclease digest of
the 15-nucleotide fragment of 5′-termini of mRNAs is shown in Fig. 14.

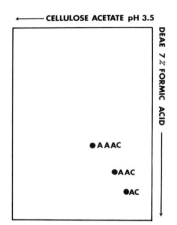

FIG. 14. Radioautography of the fingerprint of the terminal fragment of mRNA digested by T1 ribonuclease. mRNA was labeled with adenosine-^{14}C as described in Fig. 7, and the 15-nucleotide fragment was isolated as shown in Fig. 13. The mixture was digested with pancreatic RNase. The digest was concentrated, applied as a spot on a cellulose acetate strip and electrophoresed. It was electrophoresed in the second direction on DEAE paper under standard conditions. Radioactive spots were identified by radioautography. From Ilan and Ilan (1973a).

The digest was electrophoresed on cellulose acetate for the first dimension and on DEAE-paper for the second dimension. Three radioactive spots were observed by autoradiography; they were further identified as AC, AAC, and AAAC from their position in the fingerprint in relation to nonradioactive spots. This identification was further confirmed by column chromatography on DEAE-cellulose, followed by alkaline hydrolysis and identification of the nucleotides by thin-layer chromatography. No fragment of A or poly(A) terminating in U was found. Therefore, the initiation signal AUG in this mRNA does not begin immediately at the 5′ end and may be at a distance greater than 15 nucleotides. Further experiments showed that U is not incorporated into the 15-nucleotide fragment. Cytidine-^{14}C in the fragment associates only with the spots containing A, identified in Fig. 14. The mRNA population may be heterogeneous at the 5′ end, but the individual mRNAs are similar in that they all start with A and have a G at position 15. Only three oligonucleotide spots were observed. Therefore, if we assume that the fragment is heterogeneous there must be a minimum of 7 A's and a maximum of 10 A's in any one species.

We have no evidence that the first 15 nucleotides at the 5′ end of mRNA are necessary for recognition in the binding of RNA to ribosomes. Moreover, we are not sure how far the first AUG codon is from the 5′ end.

It is unlikely that in our system we are dealing with one mRNA; we are probably dealing with a heterogeneous population of mRNAs. Therefore, the fact that they all have sequence homology at the 5′ end may have an evolutionary significance. It may reflect the recognition signal for RNA polymerase in gene transcription, or it may serve as a signal for the initiation factors for binding and positioning of mRNA on ribosomes.

Recently, sequence homology at the 5′ termini of *Xenopus* polysomal mRNA was reported (Dina *et al.*, 1974). They labeled the mRNA with cyanoethylphosphate at the 5′ end. By means of hybridization they detected repetitive sequences at the 5′ end of mRNA. From the kinetics of the hybridization it was estimated that gene reiteration of DNA sequences coding for about 2000 repetitive units is located at the 5′ end of mRNA. The size of the repetitive units was estimated to be 50–60 nucleotides long.

VII. Concluding Remarks

It is obvious that genes have to be activated at some stage of development. However, there is a lag period between the appearance of the protein–gene product and the timing of its mRNA transcription in some developmental systems. Therefore, regulation of mRNA translation plays a major role in development.

Much of the current thinking and experimental design in the field of growth and differentiation is based on the model for gene expression suggested by Jacob and Monod (1961). Although this model was proved to be essentially correct for some bacterial systems, it has not been adequately tested for multicellular organisms.

Many variations and modifications of this model have been suggested for higher organisms. For insects it was first proposed by Karlson (1963) that ecdysone acts directly on the gene to produce mRNA for a specific protein enzyme, dopa decarboxylase. An inhibition of the hormonal effect by actinomycin D was interpreted as a proof for direct hormonal involvement in the transcription of DNA into mRNA. The experiments with ecdysone was performed on the blow fly *Calliphora* during puparium formation. The ligated larvae were treated with ecdysone, and the induced enzyme appeared in the epidermal cells 20 hours later. Since ecdysone is known to stimulate cell division in the epidermis, the daughter cells are the ones likely to contain the induced enzyme. Therefore, the cells treated with ecdysone are probably not those that contain high dopa decarboxylase.

A prerequisite for regulation of gene expression as put forth by Jacob and Monod is that the mRNA must be a short-lived intermediate. Thus, the synthesis of the final gene product, the protein, could be "turned on" or "turned off" by turning on or off the synthesis of mRNA. It is well established in many developing systems as well as in insect development that many mRNAs are stable. Moreover, there is usually a lag period between the synthesis of mRNA and its translation. Therefore, in cells containing stable mRNA some of which is not immediately translated, other mechanisms must be responsible for gene expression. These mechanisms must be at the translational or posttranscriptional level.

Here we have presented evidence for the regulation of the synthesis of one protein, adult cuticular protein during *Tenebrio* adult development. Our experiments show that the control of gene expression is at the translational level and involves the appearance of new tRNA and its activating enzyme. The mRNA for cuticular protein is formed well in advance but is not immediately translated. tRNA and enzyme from the differentiated stage can direct the reading of this specific mRNA. Moreover, tRNA from hormone-treated animals, added to normal ribosomes which contain mRNA for adult cuticular protein, cannot permit the synthesis of this protein.

The identification of the protein product of the cell-free system was achieved by cochromatography of the tryptic digest, together with digest of cuticular protein synthesized *in vivo*. We have also shown that it is the tRNA fraction, not a contaminant in the tRNA preparation, which is important. This was achieved by inactivation and reactivation of tRNA with tRNA-CMP-AMP-pyrophosphorylase. The fact that the enzyme fraction is also needed is interesting, because such a requirement could provide a double-filter mechanism. We have never observed more than one peak of activity of leucyl-tRNA synthetase from a chromatographic profile. In addition, we have recently purified leu-tRNA-synthetase from day 1 and day 7 to about 600-fold. The two enzyme preparations showed the same K_m values for: ATP, PP$_i$, Mg^{2+}, leucine, and day 1 tRNA. However, the day 7 enzyme differs in its ability to charge day 7 tRNA over and above day 1 enzyme. Therefore, the additional functions of this enzyme at day 7 of development might result from an alteration at the macromolecular level.

We have also shown that on purified ribosomes neither chain initiation nor chain termination of polypeptide take place. Therefore, the translational effect is at the level of chain elongation and involves a rate-limiting species of tRNA. We have shown the appearance of new isoacceptor tRNA^{Leu} which is genetically different from the five isoacceptor tRNA^{Leu} present during early development. There is no direct evidence of involvement of this subspecies of tRNA with the switch in protein synthesis, but there is indirect evidence. The timing of the appearance of new leucyl-acceptor-tRNA is correlated to the shift in protein synthesis. Also, the fact that enzyme and tRNA are required from a late developmental stage for the switch in protein synthesis may suggest the existence of a link between the acceptor activity and the switch in protein synthesis. We would like to stress that the appearance of new leucyl specific tRNA during development is not unique for insects and has been reported for many developing systems. Leucyl tRNA is in a suitable position to regulate protein synthesis. There are six code words for leucine, UUA, UUG, CUU, CUC, CUA, CUG. Each of them inserts leucine into polypeptide chain and requires tRNAs which are different from each other at least in the anticodon sequence.

We imagine that in some developmental systems the mRNAs are stable and programmed in advance. In others, some of the mRNA is stable while some is turned over. However, a group of mRNAs share a common code for a rare tRNA. The appearance of a rare tRNA either as a result of direct effect of hormone or other cell stimuli on DNA, or due to activation of preexisting tRNA will trigger the translation of these mRNAs. Since the code is degenerate, other messages, which do not share this particular code word, are independent of the hormone and of other developmental stimuli and can be translated.

Another possibility of regulation of mRNA translation is at the level of chain initiation. This is supported in our system by evidence of specificity in the formation of the 80 S initiation complex. We assume that such regulation may operate as a crude tuning on groups of mRNAs which share a specific sequence of oligonucleotides at the 5' end near the initiation site. This sequence may be recognized by a unique initiation factor. Another possibility is that a unique initiation factor recognizes a group of mRNAs which share a similar secondary structure. To test these possibilities, initiation factors must be identified and isolated, and the mRNA sequenced at the 5' region. Our efforts in these directions have been presented here.

The specificity for initiation of protein synthesis may have evolved in conjunction with evolution of differentiation. Tissue specificity for initiation of myosin mRNA translation has been demonstrated by Heywood (1969, 1970). A specific protein factor has also been shown to be required for the translation of encephalomyocarditis virus RNA in a mammalian cell-free system (Mathews, 1970; Aviv et al., 1971). It was also shown that rat liver cell sap cannot support initiation of protein synthesis with Xenopus liver ribosomes (Clemens and Tata, 1972). It may be that multipotential cells are able to translate heterologous mRNA. Xenopus oocytes when injected with 9 S hemoglobin mRNA initiate and translate the message (Gurdon et al., 1971).

ACKNOWLEDGMENTS

Research work reported in this paper was supported in part by research grants GB 30906 from the National Science Foundation and HD 06727 from the National Institute of Child Health and Human Development.

REFERENCES

Adams, J. M., and Cory, S. (1970). *Nature (London)* 227, 570.

Anderson, W. F. (1969). *Proc. Nat. Acad. Sci. U.S.* 62, 566.

Anderson, W. F., and Gilbert, J. M (1969). *Cold Spring Harbor Symp. Quant. Biol.* 34, 585.

Aviv, H., Boime, I., and Leder, P. (1971). *Proc. Nat. Acad. Sci. U.S.* 68, 2303.

Bernfield, M. R., and Mäenpää, P. H. (1971). *Cancer Res.* 31, 684.

Bhaduri, S., Chatterjee, N. K., Bose, K. K., and Gupta, N. K. (1970). *Biochem. Biophys. Res. Commun.* 40, 402.

Bishop, J. O. (1966). *Biochim. Biophys. Acta* 119, 130.

Brown, J. C., and Smith, A. E. (1970). *Nature (London)* 226, 610.

Canellakis, E. S., and Herbert, E. (1960). *Biochim. Biophys. Acta* 45, 133.

Caskey, C. T., Redfield, B., and Weissbach, H. (1967). *Arch. Biochem. Biophys.* 120, 119.

Caston, J. D. (1971). *Develop. Biol.* 24, 19.

Clemens, M. J., and Tata, J. R. (1972). *Biochim. Biophys. Acta* 269, 130.

DeWachter, R., and Fiers, W. (1969). *Nature (London)* 221, 233.

DeWachter, R., Verhassel, J. P., and Fiers, W. (1968). *Biochim. Biophys. Acta* 157, 195.

Dina, D., Meza, I., and Crippa, M. (1974). *Nature (London)* 248, 486.

Dintzis, H. M. (1961). *Proc. Nat. Acad. Sci. U.S.* 47, 247.

Fan, H., and Penman, S. (1970). *J. Mol. Biol.* 50, 655.

Fox, A. S., Kan, J., Kang, S. H., and Wallis, B. (1965). *J. Biol. Chem.* 240, 2059.

Garel, J. P., Mandel, P., Chavancy, G., and Daillie, J. (1970). *FEBS (Fed. Eur. Biochem. Soc.) Lett.* 7, 327.

Gross, P. R., and Cousineau, G. H. (1963). *Biochem. Biophys. Res. Commun.* 10, 321.

Gurdon, J. B., Lane, C. D., Woodland, H. R., and Marbaix, G. (1971) *Nature (London)* 233, 177.

Heywood, S. M. (1969). *Cold Spring Harbor Symp. Quant. Biol.* 34, 799.

Heywood, S. M. (1970). *Nature (London)* 225, 696.

Hogan, B. L. M., and Korner, A. (1968). *Biochim. Biophys. Acta* 169, 139.

Holland, J. J., Taylor, M. W., and Buck, C. A. (1967). *Proc. Nat. Acad. Sci. U.S.* 58, 2437.

Housman, D., Jacobs-Lorena, M., Rajbhandary, U. L., and Lodish, H. F. (1970). *Nature (London)* 227, 913.

Howells, A. J., Birt, L., and Finch, L. R. (1967). *J. Insect Physiol.* 13, 1221.

Hsu, W. T., and Weiss, S. B. (1969). *Proc. Nat. Acad. Sci. U.S.* 64, 345.

Ilan, J. (1968). *J Biol. Chem.* 243, 5859.

Ilan, J. (1969a). *Biochemistry* 8, 4825.

Ilan, J. (1969b). *Cold Spring Harbor Symp. Quant. Biol.* 34, 787.

Ilan, J. (1969c). *J. Cell Biol.* 43, 57A.

Ilan, J. (1971). *Fed. Proc., Fed. Amer. Soc. Exp. Biol.* 30, 1290.

Ilan, J. (1973). *J. Mol. Biol.* 77, 437.

Ilan, J., and Ilan, J. (1970). *Biochim. Biophys. Acta* **224**, 614.

Ilan, J., and Ilan, J. (1971). *Develop. Biol.* **25**, 280.

Ilan, J., and Ilan, J. (1973a). *Proc. Nat. Acad. Sci. U.S.* **70**, 1355.

Ilan, J., and Ilan, J. (1973b). *Annu. Rev. Entomol.* **18**, 167.

Ilan, J., and Ilan, J. (1973c). *Nature (London), New Biol.* **241**, 176.

Ilan, J., and Ilan, J. (1974). *In* "The Physiology of Insecta" (M. Rockstein, ed.), 2nd ed., Vol. 4, pp. 355–420. Academic Press, New York.

Ilan, J., and Lipmann, F. (1966). *Acta Biochim. Pol.* **13**, 353.

Ilan, J., and Quastel, J. H. (1966). *Biochem. J.* **100**, 448.

Ilan, J., Ilan, J., and Quastel, J. H.(1966). *Biochem. J.* **100**, 441.

Ilan, J., Ilan, J., and Patel, N. G. (1970). *J. Biol. Chem.* **245**, 1275.

Ilan, J., Ilan, J., and Patel, N. G. (1972). "Insect Juvenile Hormones" (J. J. Menn and M. Beroza, eds), p. 43. Academic Press, New York.

Jackson, R., and Hunter, T. (1970). *Nature (London)* **227**, 672.

Jacob, F., and Monod, J. (1961). *J. Mol. Biol.* **3**, 318.

Joklik, W. K., and Becker, Y. (1965). *J. Mol. Biol.* **13**, 496.

Kabat, D., and Rich, A. (1969). *Biochemistry* **8**, 3742.

Kaempfer, R. (1969). *Nature (London)* **222**, 951.

Kafatos, F. C., and Reich, J. (1968). *Proc. Nat. Acad. Sci. U.S.* **60**, 1458.

Karlson, P. (1963). *Perspect. Biol. Med.* **6**, 203.

Kerwar, S. S., Weissbach, H., and Glenner, G. (1971). *Arch. Biochem. Biophys.* **143**, 336.

Lee, J. C., and Ingram, V. M. (1967). *Science* **158**, 1330.

Lengyel, O., and Söll, D. (1969). *Bacteriol. Rev.* **33**, 264.

Lipmann, F. (1969). *Science* **164**, 1024.

Lodish, H. F. (1969). *Nature (London)* **224**, 867.

Lodish, H. F. (1970). *J. Mol. Biol.* **50**, 689.

Marks, P. A., Rifkind, R., and Danon, D. (1963). *Proc. Nat. Acad. Sci. U.S.* **50**, 336.

Mathews, M. B. (1970). *Nature (London)* **228**, 661.

Mittelman, A. (1971). *Cancer Res.* **31**, 647.

Moscona, A. A., Moscona, M. H., and Saenz, N. (1968). *Proc. Nat. Acad. Sci. U.S* **61**, 160.

Nathans, D., and Lipmann, F. (1960). *Biochim. Biophys. Acta* **43**, 126.

Neulat, M. (1967). *Biochim. Biophys. Acta* **149**, 422.

Onodera, K., and Komano, T. (1964). *Biochim. Biophys. Acta* **87**, 338.

Patel, N. G (1972). *In* "Molecular Genetic Mechanisms in Development and Aging" (M. Rockstein and G. T. Baker, eds.), p. 145. Academic Press, New York.

Prichard, P. M., Gilbert, J. M., Shafritz, D. A., and Anderson, W. F. (1970). *Nature (London)* **226**, 511.

Revel, M., Aviv (Greenshpan), H., Groner, Y., and Pollack, Y. (1970). *FEBS (Fed. Eur. Biochem. Soc.) Lett.* **9**, 213.

Schimke, R. T., Palmiter, R. D., Palacios, R., Rhoads, R. E., McKnight, S., Sullivan, D., and Summers, M. (1973). *In* "Genetic Mechanisms of Development" (F. H. Ruddle, ed.), p. 225. Academic Press, New York.

Schneiderman, H. A., and Gilbert, L. J. (1964). *Science* **143**, 325.

Scott, R. B., and Bell, E. (1964). *Science* **145**, 711.

Smith, A. E., and Marcker, K. A. (1970). *Nature (London)* **226**, 607.

Steitz, J. A. (1969). *Nature (London)* **224**, 957.

Stewart, J. A., and Papaconstantinou, J. (1967). *J. Mol. Biol.* **29**, 357.

Strehler, D. L., Hendley, D. D, and Hirsch, G. P. (1967). *Proc. Nat. Acad. Sci. U.S* **57**, 1751.

Sussman, M. (1966). *Proc. Nat. Acad. Sci. U.S.* **55**, 813.

Takeishi, K., Ukita, T., and Nishimura, S. (1968). *J. Biol. Chem.* **243**, 5761.

Taylor, M. W., Granger, G. A, Buck, C. A., and Holland, J. J. (1967). *Proc. Nat. Acad. Sci. U.S.* **57**, 1712.

Taylor, M. W., Volkers, S. A. S., Choe, B. K, and Zeikus, J. G. (1971). *Cancer Res.* **31**, 688.

Virmaux, N., Mandel, P., and Garel, J. P. (1969). *FEBS Meet.* Abstr. No. 724, p. 231.

Weisblum, B., Gonano, F., von Ehrenstein, G., and Benzer, S. (1965). *Proc. Nat. Acad. Sci. U.S.* **53**, 328.

Whelly, S. M., and Barker, K. L. (1974). *Biochemistry* **13**, 341.

Wigle, D. T., and Dixon, G. H. (1970). *Nature (London)* **227**, 676.

Wilson, D. B., and Dintzis, H. M. (1970). *Proc. Nat. Acad. Sci. U.S.* **66**, 1282.

Winslow, R. M., and Ingram, V. M (1966). *J. Biol. Chem.* **241**, 1144.

Yang, W. K., and Novelli, G. D. (1968). *Biochem. Biophys. Res. Commun.* **31**, 534.

Yang, W. K. (1971). *Cancer Res.* **31**, 639.

Yoshida, A., Watanabe, S., and Morris, J. (1970). *Proc. Nat. Acad. Sci. U.S.* **67**, 1600.

CHAPTER 5

CHEMICAL AND STRUCTURAL CHANGES WITHIN CHICK ERYTHROCYTE NUCLEI INTRODUCED INTO MAMMALIAN CELLS BY CELL FUSION

R. Appels* and Nils R. Ringertz

INSTITUTE FOR MEDICAL CELL RESEARCH AND GENETICS
MEDICAL NOBEL INSTITUTE, KAROLINSKA INSTITUTET
STOCKHOLM, SWEDEN

I. Introduction

The chick erythrocyte is a terminally differentiated cell and its nucleus is very low in activity related to macromolecular synthesis. The inactivation occurs gradually during erythropoiesis and is paralleled by changes in nuclear composition and a condensation of the chromatin. Several steps in this process are reversed in chick erythrocyte nuclei introduced into the cytoplasm of mammalian tissue culture cells by means of cell fusion (Harris, 1965, 1967). The term "reactivation" was introduced by Harris (1965) to describe these changes, and although it covers a wide range of phenomena (as will be seen in this paper), it is an appro-

---

* Present address: Division of Plant Industry, CSIRO, P.O.Box 1600, Canberra, A.C.T., Australia.

priate one in relation to the end result. Convincing data have been presented that DNA of the biologically inactive nuclei found in chick erythrocytes does eventually become available for the expression of a chick phenotype as a result of the reactivation reaction. Parameters of chick phenotype which have been established include the biochemical identification chick hypoxanthine guanine phosphoribosyl transferase (Harris and Cook, 1969; Boyd and Harris, 1973; Klinger and Shin, 1974) and biological assays for chick cell surface antigens, diphtheria toxin receptors and enzymes, such as thymidine kinase, adenine phosphoribosyl transferase (Harris *et al.*, 1969; Deák *et al.*, 1972; Clemens, 1972; Dendy and Harris, 1973). Evidence has also been presented that chick DNA can complement a missing regulatory type function to allow reexpression of a previously absent mammalian marker from the respective mammalian cell, e.g., reexpression of mouse thymidine kinase (Boyd and Harris, 1973) and mouse C5 complement (Levy *et al.*, 1973). The question of expression of a specialized chick phenotype as a result of the reactivation reaction is an open one and has been discussed previously (Ringertz and Bolund, 1974a; Ringertz and Savage, 1975).

The data reviewed in this paper will deal with recent studies carried out on the chick erythrocyte nucleus as it undergoes the reactivation reaction. The emphasis will be on macromolecular and structural changes within the erythrocyte nucleus. For a more detailed discussion of phenotypic expression in heterokaryons and "model" systems for reactivating chick erythrocyte nuclei, the reader is referred to Ringertz and Bolund (1974a).

II. Properties of "Inactive" Chick Erythrocyte Nuclei

Since the nuclei of mature chick erythrocytes are the starting point of the reactivation reaction, we describe first the known chemical and biological features of this nucleus (for a detailed review, see Ringertz and Bolund, 1974b).

The chick erythrocyte nucleus has its chromatin in a condensed state without an identifiable nucleolus. The DNA in the condensed chromatin is relatively stable to heat denaturation, under defined experimental conditions (T_m 85–90°), compared to the DNA of active nuclei in growing cells (T_m 75–80°; Rigler *et al.*, 1969; Bolund *et al.*, 1969b). The DNA content per nucleus is 10–15% of a G_1 HeLa cell nucleus while the histone:DNA ratio of its chromatin is comparable to that of HeLa chromatin (approximately 1.0:1.0). The total protein:DNA ratio of chick erythrocyte nuclei is rather low at approximately 1.3:1.0 compared to a value of approximately 3.6:1.0 for actively growing cells (Dingman and Sporn, 1964). Consistent with these figures are the cytochemical measurements carried out on cells at different stages of avian erythropoiesis which show that the nuclear dry mass:DNA ratio decreases as cells mature to erythrocytes (Kernell et al., 1971).

Besides the low DNA and protein values, chick erythrocyte nuclei also have a number of macromolecular markers not found in mammalian nuclei. Thus cytochemically, specific antigens (precise chemical nature unknown) can be identified (Ringertz et al., 1971; Carlsson et al., 1974a) while biochemically the f1 (HI) group of histones are the most characteristic proteins of chick erythrocyte nuclei. Within the latter group the f2c (HV) histone is tissue specific to the erythrocyte (Stedman and Stedman, 1950), while the remaining f1 histones are electrophoretically distinguishable from the mammalian ones. The chick histones are probably also immunologically distinguishable from mammalian histones (U. Plagens, personal communication; Sotirov and Johns, 1972; Bustin and Stollar, 1973). It should be mentioned here that hemoglobin is not a significant nuclear protein in chick erythrocyte nuclei (Small and Davies, 1970). The small quantity of nonhistone proteins in chick erythrocyte nuclei has been analyzed on SDS gels (Elgin and Bonner, 1970; Shelton and Neelin, 1971; Appels et al., 1973; Harlow et al., 1972). Most of the nonhistone bands present in other cell types were identified, although the chick erythrocyte nuclei contained relatively fewer proteins of molecular weight approximately 50,000 and contained additional high molecular weight proteins (e.g., the band called χ by Elgin and Bonner, 1970).

Macromolecular synthesis in chick erythrocyte nuclei is among the lowest found in eukaryote cell nuclei. The usual source of chick erythrocytes, namely 13–15-day chick embryos, show low but detectable levels of RNA synthesis, which become more significant in erythrocytes from younger embryos. DNA synthesis, on the other hand, appears to have stopped completely in mature erythrocytes (Williams, 1972). The nuclei of these cells, as well as those of adult erythrocytes, contain low but significant levels of an RNA polymerase which has been identified as being of the α-amanitin-sensitive type (i.e., the nucleoplasmic B enzyme; Schechter, 1973). Other nucleoplasmic enzymes, such as NAD pyrophosphorylase and histone acetylase, have also been measured in chick erythrocyte nuclei (Zentgraf et al., 1971; Allfrey, 1970). The absolute levels of these enzymes are, as indicated above, low and in general provide a good "base" line against which to measure possible increases during reactivation.

The nuclear membranes of chick erythrocyte nuclei resemble those of mammalian nuclei with respect to gross protein, phospholipid, nonpolar lipids, and RNA content (Franke et al., 1970; Zentgraf et al., 1971). The two types of membranes also appear to be similar with respect to individual lipid components (Kleinig et al., 1971). The proteins of the nuclear membranes, however, are not well characterized and since they constitute 75% of the dry weight of the nuclear membrane they remain an important possible source of difference between chick and mammalian nuclei.

III. Morphological Changes in Reactivating Chick Erythrocyte Nuclei

A. LIGHT MICROSCOPICAL STUDIES

Harris' early description of chick erythrocyte nuclei reactivation was in part based on the marked morphological changes that occur within these nuclei. Thus the diameter of the nucleus increased and the chromatin appeared to become decondensed. Cytochemically this has been more accurately described as resulting from an increase in dry weight of the nuclei (Bolund et al., 1969b), a reduction in the stability of DNA to heat denaturation and in increased accessibility of the DNA phosphate groups to binding by acridine orange (Bolund et al., 1969b). Figure 1 shows the chick erythrocyte nucleus at various stages of the reactivation reaction as it occurs in all tissue culture cells examined so far but illustrated here in primary cultures of muscle tissue. In the following discussion, cells of the type shown in Fig. 1 containing two different types of nuclei (in this case chick and mammalian nuclei) will be referred to as heterokaryons.

B. ELECTRON MICROSCOPICAL STUDIES

Several laboratories have carried out electron microscopical analyses on chick erythrocyte nuclei at various stages of the reactivation reaction (Schneeberger and Harris, 1966; Lindberg, 1974; Dupuy-Coin et al., 1975). These studies showed the chick nucleus to be introduced into the mammalian cell with an intact inner and outer nuclear membrane and its chromatin in a highly condensed state. The electron microscopical studies indicate that a large number of erythrocytes lyse and lose their cytoplasm before fusion occurs. Some chick cytoplasmic material (hemoglobin) is, however, introduced into heterokaryons (Carlsson et al., 1974b; Zakai et al., 1974). Studies of the ultrastructure of erythrocyte nuclei in heterokaryons at different times after fusion confirmed that decondensation of the chick chromatin occurred and that a nucleolus developed late in the reactivation. Figures 2, 3, and 4 show the chick erythrocyte nuclei at various stages of the reactivation reaction.

IV. Fate of Chick Nuclear Material

Until recently the fate of chick nuclei was considered to be that they disappeared as an identifiable entity when the mammalian cell into which

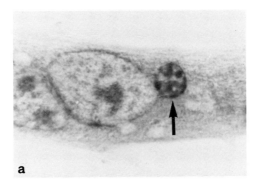

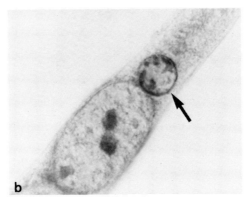

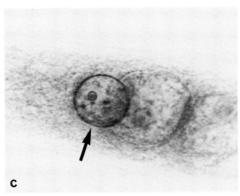

FIG. 1. Stages of chick erythrocyte nucleus reactivation after introduction into rat myotubes by cell fusion. Rat myotubes were derived from a primary culture of embryonic muscle tissue. Unstained preparations were photographed in a UV microscope. Times post-fusion at which preparations were examined were (a) 3 hours; (b) 19 hours; (c) 92 hours. Arrows indicate erythrocyte nuclei (S.-A. Carlsson, R. E. Savage, and N. R. Ringertz, unpublished results).

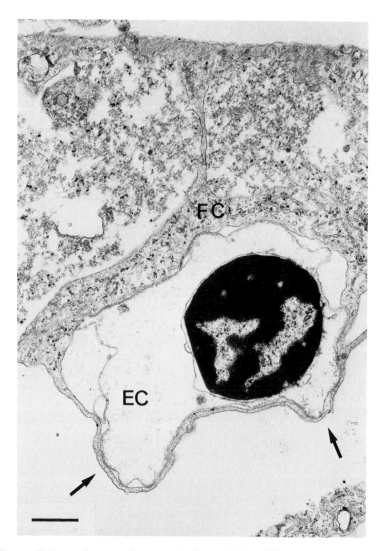

Fig. 2. Chick erythrocyte ghost at the time of fusion. The erythrocyte cytoplasm
(EC) is lysed, and the whole ghost is engulfed by a cytoplasmic process (arrows)
continuous with the fibroblast cytoplasm (FC). ×13,000. Scale shown represents
1 μm. From Dupuy-Coin *et al.* (1975).

the chick nuclei had been introduced underwent mitosis and cell division.
Thus at mitosis of the heterokaryon, chick nuclei in general were thought
to undergo premature chromatin condensation (Schwartz *et al.*, 1971)
in accordance with the phenomenon described by Johnson *et al.* (1970).
This is not in fact always the case as shown by single-cell analyses

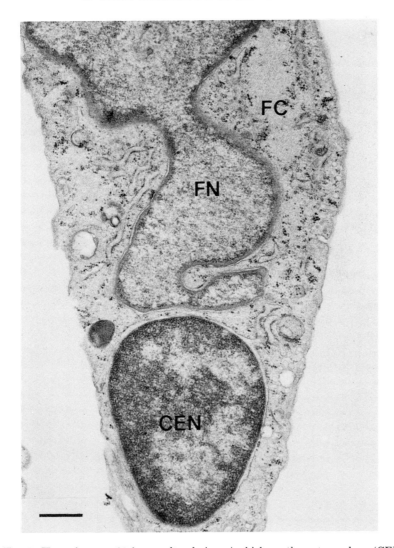

Fɪɢ. 3. Heterokaryon, 24 hours after fusion. A chick erythrocyte nucleus (CEN) and a host, fibroblast nucleus (FN) are observed within the fibroblast cytoplasm (FC). ×15,000. Scale shown represents 1 μm. From Dupuy-Coin *et al.* (1975).

carried out by Appels *et al.* (1975a). Figure 5 shows one such analysis in which a HeLa × chick erythrocyte heterokaryon is seen to divide and at least one of the original chick nuclei is clearly identifiable in the daughter cells. Independent evidence from analyzing populations of heterokaryons at various times post-fusion indicated that such transfers must occur for more than 50% of the chick nuclei in dividing hetero-

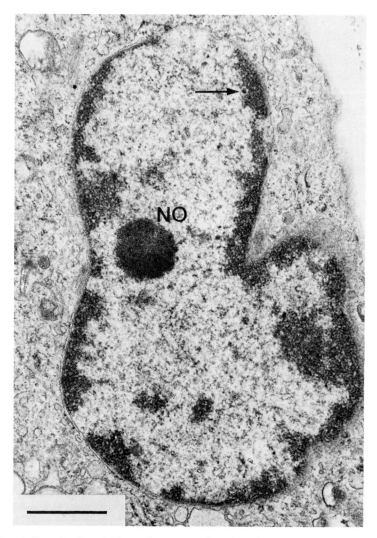

FIG. 4. Reactivating chick erythrocyte nucleus in a heterokaryon, 24 hours after fusion. The chromatin has resumed a dispersed state. A new nucleolus (NO) is visible, purely fibrillar in structure. A perichromatin granule (arrow) is observed. ×22,000. Scale shown represents 1 μm. From Dupuy-Coin *et al.* (1975).

karyons. The fact that chick nuclei could be carried through a mitosis, intact, demonstrated an additional phenomenon of rapid nuclear swelling in the early G_1 period of the daughter cells. This rapid reactivation post mitosis was consistent with early observations on cell division which

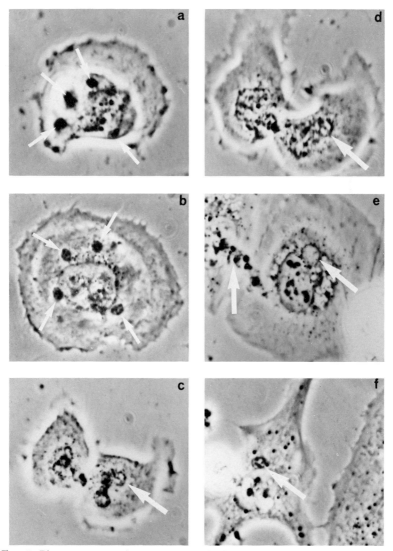

Fig. 5. Phase-contrast microscopy on a single HeLa × chick erythrocyte hetero-karyon at (a) the time of fusion; (b) 5 hours post-fusion; (c) 10 hours post-fusion; (d) 11 hours post-fusion; (e) 21 hours post-fusion. Also in (f) is a heterokaryon in the same culture, 21 hours post-fusion, which did not undergo a division. The arrows indicate chick erythrocyte nuclei which were clearly identifiable—the arrow on the left side of figure (e) shows the position of two chick nuclei that could not be identified with absolute certainty (Appels *et al.,* 1975a).

showed a large influx of macromolecules into G_1 nuclei just after cell division (Richards and Bajer, 1961; Prescott and Goldstein, 1968).

The eventual fate of chick nuclear material is to be eliminated from the mammalian cell in which it was originally present as the latter continues to divide. Kao (1973) found metaphase cells with both mammalian and chick chromosomes in a heterokaryon culture approximately a week post fusion. Subsequent divisions of the synkaryons (mononucleate hybrid cells derived from heterokaryons where both mammalian and chick nuclei entered mitosis synchronously) resulted in a preferential elimination of chick chromosomes. A certain amount of chick DNA can be retained by the synkaryon if it complements a gene deficiency in the mammalian "host" cell and helps the hybrid cell survive on selective media on which the mammalian cell would otherwise die. It has thus been shown in synkaryons where chick DNA complements a hypoxanthine guanine phosphoribosyl transferase (HGPRT) deficiency (Boyd and Harris, 1973; Klinger and Shin, 1974) or an adenine deficiency (Kao, 1973) that the elimination of chick chromosomes goes essentially to completion except for the retention of the chick DNA selected for. Furthermore, this chick DNA which is retained is rapidly lost when the selective pressure is removed as shown by the reversion of synkaryons from, for example, HGPRT$^+$ to HGPRT$^-$ with a frequency of 20% compared with an average back mutation rate of approximately 0.0001% (Schwartz et al., 1971). It is interesting that shortly after selective pressure on the above HGPRT$^+$ synkaryons is removed the chick HGPRT gene shows a modulating behavior (Klinger and Shin, 1974)—over extended periods without selection, however, the chick gene is permanently lost from the synkaryon. The reason for the preferential elimination of chick chromosomes is not clear but may reflect on species incompatability in the system.

V. Changes in Protein Composition within Reactivating Chick Nuclei

A. Cytochemical Analyses

As pointed out in a previous section, the reactivation reaction in chick erythrocyte nuclei is accompanied by a 2- to 3-fold increase in dry weight of the respective nuclei. Considering the contribution proteins make to the dry weight of a nucleus (approximately 80%) the question we try to answer now is what types of proteins contribute to the dry weight increase of reactivating chick erythrocyte nuclei.

Analysis of nuclei by microspectrophotometric means after allowing available protein to react with acidic dyes such as sulfaflavine (Leeman and Ruch, 1972) and naphthol yellow (Deitsch, 1955) or with reagents such as dansyl chloride [to assay ϵ and α NH$_2$ groups (Rosselet and Ruch (1968)] have shown that the overall protein content of reactivating chick nuclei increases 2- to 3-fold largely owing to an early accumulation of nonhistone type proteins (Appels et al., 1975b). Autoradiographic analysis in fact show that newly made proteins, labeled by leucine-H^3, start to accumulate in the reactivating chick nuclei within 1–2 hours post fusion (Appels et al., 1974a). Proteins synthesized in the mammalian cell *before* fusion also accumulated rapidly in reactivating chick nuclei as shown in pulse-chase type experiments (Goto and Ringertz, 1974; Appels et al., 1974a).

Specific nonhistone type proteins accumulating in reactivated chick nuclei which have been identified include a DNA repair enzyme (Darzynkiewicz and Chelmicka-Szorc, 1972) and the T-antigen from SV40-transformed cells (Rosenqvist et al., 1975), (Fig. 6a). In addition, a mammalian nucleolar antigen and a mammalian nucleoplasmic antigen (Ringertz et al., 1971), the precise nature of which is unknown, have been shown to accumulate in reactivating chick erythrocyte nuclei. The important characteristics shared by these proteins and antigens is that they are normally located in the mammalian nucleus and that those molecules accumulating in reactivated chick nuclei were experimentally identified as mammalian in origin. Other specific proteins identified in the reactivating chick erythrocyte nuclei include RNA polymerases A and B (Carlsson et al., 1973), but whether these are of chick or mammalian origin, or a mixture of both species is not known. As discussed before, nonreactivated chick erythrocyte nuclei have a low basal level of RNA polymerase activity.

A "new" chick component which appears in reactivating chick nuclei is a specific nucleolar antigen (once again the precise chemical nature of this antigen is unknown) which is found in most chick nuclei, but not in nonreactivated chick erythrocyte nuclei. Whether this is an uncovering of a preexisting antigen or the accumulation of a new chick protein is not altogether clear. It is interesting, however, that this antigen also appears in the mammalian nucleus (Ringertz et al., 1971) and may thus reflect the new synthesis of chick molecules. These molecules are probably synthesized in the cytoplasm but then migrate into both chick and mammalian nuclei.

Specific nonhistone type proteins which do *not* accumulate in reactivating chick erythrocyte nuclei include a mammalian cytoplasmic antigen (Ringertz et al., 1971), lactate dehydrogenase, isocitrate dehydrogenase, and malate dehydrogenase (Appels et al., 1975b) (Fig. 6b). The common feature of these proteins is that they are cytoplasmic and not normally resident in mammalian nuclei.

An important conclusion from the data discussed in this section is that mammalian proteins transfer into reactivating chick erythrocyte nuclei in a *nonrandom* fashion with only nucleospecific proteins appearing in the chick nuclei.

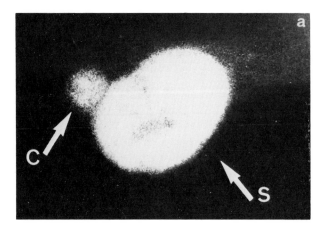

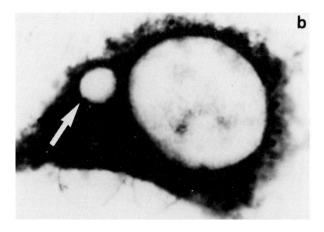

FIG. 6. Cytochemical assays for specific cellular proteins in a mammalian cell × chick erythrocyte heterokaryons. (a) The mammalian cell used to form heterokaryon was a human fibroblast transformed by SV40 (WiSV40) with the characteristic SV40 T-antigen being assayed by a fluorescent antibody binding technique. C is the reactivated chick erythrocyte nucleus, and S the WiSV40 nucleus, the cytoplasm of the cell shows no fluorescence. From Rosenqvist *et al.* (1975). (b) The mammalian cell used to form a heterokaryon was a HeLa cell; lactate dehydrogenase activity was assayed histochemically, the deposit of reduced nitro tetrazolium indicating the sites of enzyme activity. From Appels *et al.* (1975b).

B. BIOCHEMICAL ANALYSES

To analyze nuclear proteins other than the ones for which specific cytochemical assays could be developed, the reactivated chick erythrocyte nuclei have been isolated, purified, and analyzed by biochemical procedures. The nuclei were prepared from heterokaryons 15 hours post fusion at a time when relatively little DNA synthesis is occurring in reactivated chick erythrocyte nuclei. It should be noted at the start of this discussion that newly synthesized proteins appearing in reactivated chick erythrocyte nuclei in the first 20 hours post fusion are considered to be of mammalian origin. In all systems examined so far there is no evidence for new chick proteins appearing before 30–40 hours post fusion (Harris *et al.*, 1969; Ringertz *et al.*, 1971; Deák *et al.*, 1972; Appels *et al.*, 1974a). The procedure for isolating and purifying reactivated chick erythrocyte nuclei is shown in Fig. 7 (Goto and Ringertz, 1974). When carried out on a large scale, approximately 10^6 reactivated chick erythro-

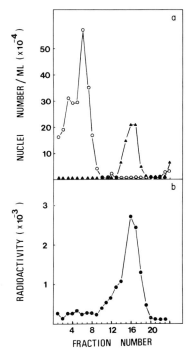

FIG. 7. Isolation of reactivated chick erythrocyte nuclei. (a) Identification of nuclei by phase microscopy in fractions from a 1–2 M sucrose gradient collected from the bottom of the tube. Nuclei were isolated from mouse L cell × chick erythrocyte heterokaryons 21 hours post-fusion and centrifuged in the sucrose gradient at 3000 rpm in a SW 25 rotor for 12 minutes. O——O, L cell nuclei; ▲——▲, reactivated chick erythrocyte nuclei. (b) Recentrifugation of the peak of chick erythrocyte nuclei with an analysis of fractions for radioactivity in acid-insoluble material. The source of radioactivity was ³H-labeled leucine added at the time of fusion. From Goto and Ringertz (1974).

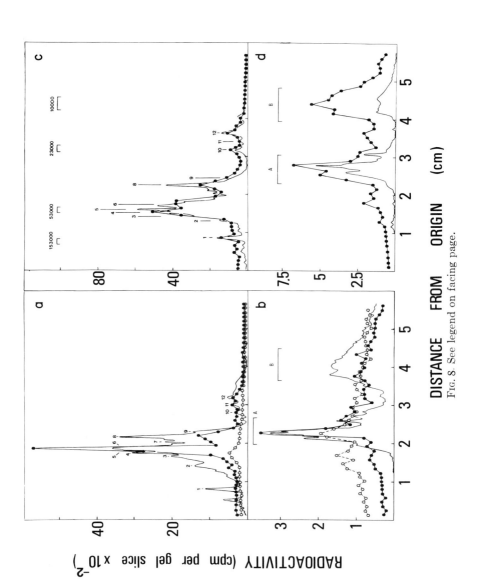

DISTANCE FROM ORIGIN (cm)

Fig. 8. See legend on facing page.

cyte nuclei could be recovered for analysis with a 5–15% *chemical* contamination level of HeLa nuclear material. The contamination problem has been examined in detail by microscopical analyses and various types of mixing experiments (Goto and Ringertz, 1974; Appels *et al.*, 1974b).

Analyses of radioactive nuclear proteins on hydroxyapatite columns (MacGillivray *et al.*, 1972) showed that both newly synthesized protein and proteins synthesized before fusion accumulated in reactivating chick erythrocyte nuclei (Appels *et al.*, 1974b). Similar conclusions were drawn from analyses of whole nuclei labeled with ^{3}H-labeled leucine (Appels *et al.*, 1974a; Goto and Ringertz, 1974) and indicated that the deposition of nuclear proteins in nuclei was not closely linked to their synthesis. Further analyses of nonhistone protein on SDS gels showed that a wide range of proteins appeared in the reactivating chick nuclei with newly synthesized protein and protein synthesized before fusion yielding similar patterns. Interestingly, proteins with a molecular weight of approximately 60,000 or less were enriched for in chick nuclei relative to the pattern found for radioactive protein from HeLa nuclei (Fig. 8a). These proteins are in fact initially low in nonreactivated chick erythrocyte nuclei apparently reduced during differentiation as judged from published analyses of chick erythrocyte nuclei when the nonhistone patterns are compared with those from nuclei of active cells (discussed in Section II). Within the low molecular weight group of proteins which appeared in reactivating chick erythrocyte nuclei, some proteins present in HeLa nuclei were not found in the chick nuclei (group B proteins from hydroxyapatite fraction III, Fig. 8b). Although the analysis of phosphoproteins (Teng *et al.*, 1971; Rickwood *et al.*, 1973) has not yet been carried out, the data obtained so far appear in general to be consistent with observations made on nuclear proteins in "activated" phase III fibroblasts

---

FIG. 8. Sodium dodecyl sulfate (SDS) gel analysis of partially fractionated nuclear proteins from purified reactivated chick erythrocyte nuclei (isolated 15 hours postfusion). Nuclear proteins were fractionated by hydroxyapatite chromatography into fraction I (histones), fraction II (most of nonhistone), and fraction III (a small amount of nonhistones cochromatographing with DNA). ^{3}H-labeled leucine was added to HeLa cells before fusion and to respective heterokaryon cultures post fusion in the analyses shown. (a) Fraction II proteins and (b) fraction III proteins from reactivated chick erythrocyte nuclei; (c) fraction II proteins and (d) fraction III proteins from HeLa nuclei isolated from the same heterokaryon culture. ●——●, Radioactivity in gel slices; ——, densitometer trace from carrier HeLa nuclear proteins stained with Coomassie blue. For the analysis of reactivated chick erythrocyte nuclei a base line of radioactivity for contaminating HeLa nuclear material was obtained by mixing experiments in which nonreactivated chick erythrocyte nuclei were reisolated after mixing with radioactive HeLa nuclei and cell debris (○——○). From Appels *et al.* (1974b).

(Rovera and Baserga, 1971; Tsuboi and Baserga, 1972; Choe and Rose, 1974), "activation" of nonproliferative microplasmodia of *Physarum polycephalum* (Le Stourgeon *et al.*, 1973), hormone stimulation of target tissues (Shelton and Allfrey, 1970; Teng and Hamilton, 1969; Barker, 1971; Ruddon and Rainey, 1970; Spelsberg *et al.*, 1973), and studies on avian erythroid maturation (for example, see Elgin and Bonner, 1970; Shelton and Neelin, 1971; Ringertz and Bolund, 1974b).

The histone proteins present in 15-hour reactivated chick erythrocyte nuclei have to data been examined only with regard to identifying the types present, in particular the newly synthesized ones (Appels *et al.*, 1974b). Chemical modification patterns have as yet not been examined. An analysis of histones on standard histone gels (Fig. 9) showed that

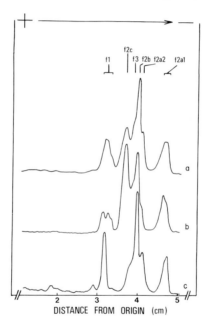

Fig. 9. Analysis of histones isolated from nuclei using 0.25 *N* HCl. Protein was analyzed on standard (low pH) polyacrylamide gels. (a) Histones from 15-hour-reactivated chick erythrocyte nuclei; (b) histones from the original nonreactivated chick erythrocyte nuclei; (c) HeLa nuclear histones prepared from the same heterokaryon culture used to prepare reactivated chick erythrocyte nuclei. From Appels *et al.* (1974b).

(1) in the f2c histone peak there was a marked reduction, which was actually the result of an absolute loss of this histone as shown by estimates of yields of histone from a known number of nuclei; (2) the f1 histone pattern was altered from that found in the nonreactivated chick

erythrocyte nuclei. The latter observation was most readily accounted
for by assuming that the mammalian f1 histone accumulated in reactivating chick erythrocyte nuclei. That this was the case was shown by labeling studies. The analyses in Fig. 10 showed that radioactivity appeared
in the histone fractions and that f1 hsitone was in fact preferentially
labeled when either leucine-³H or lysine-³H were used as radioactive pre-

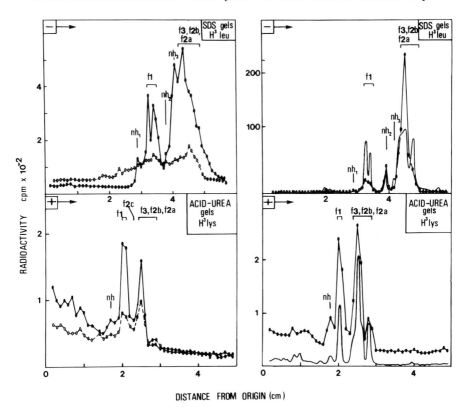

DISTANCE FROM ORIGIN (cm)

Fig. 10. Distribution of radioactivity on histones from 15-hour-reactivated chick
erythrocyte nuclei. Left panel shows the analyses from reactivated chick erythrocyte
nuclei; right panel shows analyses from HeLa nuclei in the same experiment. Radioactivity was supplied as ³H-labeled leucine before and after fusion for the sodium
dodecyl sulfate (SDS) gel analyses shown, and it was supplied as ³H-labeled lysine
in the post-fusion period only in the acid–urea gel analyses. ●——●, Radioactivity
per gel slice; ——, densitometer trace of carrier HeLa nuclear proteins stained with
Coomassie blue; ○--○, a base line of radioactivity in preparations of reactivated
chick erythrocyte nuclei due to low levels of contamination by HeLa nuclear material. The base line was determined in mixing experiments where nonreactivated
chick erythrocyte nuclei were reisolated after mixing with radioactive HeLa nuclei
and cell debris. From R. Appels, L. Bolund, and N. R. Ringertz, unpublished
observations.

cursors. Similar labeling patterns of f1 histone have also been observed in mammalian G_1 or G_0 cells (Appels and Ringertz, 1974). The SDS gel analyses of the histone fraction recovered from hydroxyapatite showed some nonhistone proteins, and one of these (nh3, see Fig. 10) was also preferentially labeled in 15-hour-reactivated chick erythrocyte nuclei when compared to the labeling pattern of the same fraction from mammalian nuclei (see Fig. 10).

VI. Changes in Nucleic Acid Metabolism

A. RNA SYNTHESIS

Among the earliest changes that occur within the reactivating chick erythrocyte nuclei is that RNA synthesis starts from the chick DNA template (Harris, 1967). The enzyme which can be assayed in the reactivating chick erythrocyte nuclei within 24 hours post fusion is the α-amanitin-sensitive RNA polymerase (RNA polymerase B), and this may be the enzyme responsible for the RNA synthesis observed (Carlsson *et al.*, 1973). Some evidence has been presented that the first type of RNA which is synthesized in the reactivating chick erythrocyte nucleus is polydisperse, high molecular weight RNA remaining within the nucleus until nucleolar development occurs (Harris *et al.*, 1969; Sidebottom and Harris, 1969; Deák *et al.*, 1972; Deák, 1973). While the absence of ribosomal RNA components in this nuclear RNA is consistent with only the RNA polymerase B enzyme being present (Zylber and Penman, 1971; Reeder and Roeder, 1972; Cramer *et al.*, 1974), it should be pointed out that the above polydisperse RNA was not characterized. The fact that the RNA is not transported from the reactivated chick erythrocyte nucleus into the cytoplasm of the heterokaryon at early times post fusion indicates that the RNA made is analogous to that synthesized in the nuclei of avian polychromatic erythrocytes (Attardi *et al.*, 1966; Scherrer *et al.*, 1966). When nucleoli develop in the reactivating chick erythrocyte nuclei, ribosomal RNA appears to be synthesized (Harris *et al.*, 1969), presumably made by the α-amanitin-resistant RNA polymerase (RNA polymerase A), which can be assayed at this later stage of reactivation (Carlsson *et al.*, 1973).

B. DNA SYNTHESIS

Two types of DNA synthesis have been identified to occur in reactivated chick erythrocyte nuclei, namely, repair synthesis (Darzynkiewicz and Chelmicka-Szorc, 1972) and replication leading to a doubling of DNA content (Harris, 1967; Bolund *et al.*, 1969b). The actual time post fusion when DNA synthesis starts in a reactivated chick nucleus appears to depend on two factors. (1) A certain degree of chromatin decondensation and protein accumulation appears to be necessary before DNA synthesis can start (Harris, 1967; Bolund et al., 1969b). (2) DNA synthesis must be occurring in the mammalian nucleus of the respective heterokaryon before DNA synthesis starts in the reactivated chick nucleus (Johnson and Harris, 1969). Generally by 15–20 hours post fusion these two conditions are satisfied, as will be discussed later.

VII. Cause–Effect Relationships

Although our knowledge of the changes that occur during the reactivation of avian erythrocytes in heterokaryons is incomplete an attempt will be made to analyze possible cause–effect relationships. We shall examine the order in which some major events occur during the reactivation process as well as evidence relating to the biochemical nature and cellular localization of possible rate-limiting factors. Overall, the evidence accumulated to date indicates that one event during the reactivation may depend on other, independent, events, thus leading to the reactivation of the chick erythrocyte genome. Before discussing such data, however, we would like to point out some general problems in analyzing published experiments. First, the fusion of most erythrocytes with the mammalian cell takes place during a time period of approximately 100 minutes; second, the reactivation process is not synchronous in all cells. These factors thus make it difficult to establish a precise time sequence in which different events occur. Third, the methods used to detect different phenomena vary with respect to their sensitivity.

A. TIME SEQUENCE OF EVENTS

Table I summarizes the known data relating to changes in reactivating chick erythrocyte nuclei with respect to the approximate time post fusion that they can be observed. The data are based primarily on HeLa × chick erythrocyte heterokaryons, but similar changes have been observed also in other types of erythrocyte heterokaryons. In the first 15 hours post fusion at least four major events occur, namely: (a) dispersion of the tightly packed chromatin of the inactive erythrocyte nucleus, (b) marked changes in the physical and chemical properties of the DNA component of the nucleoprotein (DNP) complex, (c) protein accumulation, and (d) RNA synthesis from chick DNA. Three of these events, namely, chromatin dispersion, protein accumulation, and RNA synthesis seem to be interrelated. The dispersion of chromatin and the accumulation of protein occur gradually over a 24–48-hour period while the rate of RNA synthesis accelerates in direct proportion to nuclear enlargement (Harris, 1967; Carlsson et al., 1973, 1974b). With the aid of autoradiography an uptake of labeled protein can be detected within the first hour after fusion. The earliest time point at which stimulation of RNA synthesis has been detected is 3 hours post fusion. This suggests that protein

TABLE I

DATA RELATING TO CHANGES IN REACTIVATING CHICK
ERYTHROCYTE NUCLEI VS TIME POST FUSION

Time post fusion (hours)	Changes in chick erythrocyte nucleus after introduction into mammalian cell	Events in host mammalian cell
0–1	Main fusion period with chick nuclei introduced into mammalian cytoplasm. Chromatin of nuclei condensed; DNA content = 10–15% of G_1 HeLa nucleus. Histone: DNA approx 1.1:1. Marker proteins = f2c histone and chick specific nuclear antigens	Mammalian cell into which chick nucleus was introduced may undergo division. Chick nuclei per se can be transferred as cytoplasmic particles or are lost as a result of degradation, premature chromosome condensation, and/ or nuclear fusion
1–15	Accumulation of mammalian protein (several identified). Loss of some chick protein. RNA synthesis is initiated (remains in nucleus). Nucleus undergoes marked structural changes as indicated by reduced T_m of chick DNA, increased acridine orange binding, increase in mass	
15–25	Initiation of DNA synthesis. Continued accumulation of protein	
25–40	Completion of DNA synthesis. Plateau in general protein accumulation. RNA transferred to cytoplasm. Nucleolar development and rRNA synthesis. Expression of some chick "household" genes	
40 onward	Synkaryon formation. Expression of chick genes. Rapid loss of chick DNA in multiplying synkaryons. A small piece of chick DNA may be retained if it complements a deficiency in the mammalian host cell	

uptake may actually precede the acceleration of RNA synthesis. It is possible, however, that the methods of detecting an increased RNA synthesis in intact heterokaryons are less sensitive than are the methods for detecting a protein increase in isolated nuclei. Dispersion of the chromatin is observed within 8 hours in the UV microscope but is difficult to quantify. In the electron microscope studies chromatin dispersion becomes manifest in many nuclei examined 3 hours post fusion. The changes in the properties of DNA as reflected in an increased capacity to bind intercalating dyes have been measured within 14 hours after fusion but the early time course has not been studied. It is possible that the altered dye binding properties of DNA during reactivation reflects the dispersion of chromatin observed in the UV and electron microscopes since condensation of chromatin during erythrocyte maturation (Kernell et al., 1971) and spermiogenesis (Gledhill *et al.*, 1966) are paralleled by a marked decrease in acridine orange binding capacity of the chromatin.

Some of the events discussed above can be induced in erythrocyte nuclei in cell-free systems. Although such systems are potentially valuable in the analysis of the molecular basis of the reactivation process, there are reasons to examine critically how relevant they are for the *in vivo* situation. Since these problems have been discussed in detail elsewhere (for references, see Ringertz and Bolund, 1974b), only a short summary will be given of the phenomena involved. Chromatin dispersion and nuclear swelling can be rapidly induced in isolated chick erythrocyte nuclei by lowering the ionic strength and/or reducing the concentration of divalent metal ions. Similar manipulations also induce changes in the ability of erythrocyte nuclei to bind intercalating dyes, such as acridine orange, alter the thermal stability of the DNA, and induce other changes that appear to be similar to those that occur *in vivo* in heterokaryons. These observations initially suggested to us that changes in the ionic composition in or around the erythrocyte nucleus could be a factor in the initiation of the reactivation (Ringertz, 1969). Although this possibility still exists, it now appears that the interpretation of acridine orange binding to fixed chromatin is more complex than expected. Although acridine orange binding reflects chromatin compaction, the binding of the dye and possibly its fluorescence characteristics are also affected by the way in which cells attach to their substratum, cell-to-cell interaction, and physical factors not directly related to the state of chromatin condensation. These observations make interpretation of changes in acridine orange binding difficult. Nucleoprotein changes of the type observed in model systems, although possibly necessary prerequisites, are not sufficient in themselves to induce RNA synthesis in inactive erythrocyte nuclei (L. Bolund and N. R. Ringertz, unpublished observations). Although erythrocyte nuclei contain some RNA polymerase activity, there is no direct evidence that a conformational change in the nucleoprotein or a sudden availability of the substrates in themselves are sufficient to activate transcription. Using a cytochemical assay for RNA polymerase, Moore and Ringertz (1973) found that erythrocyte nuclei do not synthesize RNA when supplied with a substrate. Similar observations were made by Hilder and MacLean (1974) in a study with nuclei isolated from *Xenopus* erythrocytes. These authors were able to induce RNA synthesis by adding exogenous *Escherichia coli* polymerase and modifying the ionic environment within physiological limits. Thompson and McCarthy (1968) and Leake *et al.* (1972) have, however, been able to induce RNA synthesis without adding exogenous bacterial polymerase by incubating isolated erythrocyte nuclei in cytoplasmic fractions from cells actively synthesizing RNA. Similar experiments in this laboratory, however, have so far failed to reproduce this phenomenon. Instead we have found that the erythrocyte nuclei, in spite of a marked swelling, frequently decrease in dry mass and then lyse (L. Bolund and N. R. Ringertz, unpublished observations).

On the basis of the considerations listed above, it appears likely that early migration of protein, most likely nonhistone protein, may be among the first if not the first event in the reactivation phenomenon. Further evidence in favor of this view point is discussed in the following sections.

B. Competition for Rate-Limiting Factors

When more than one chick nucleus is present in the mammalian host cell, the rate of reactivation is slowed down (Carlsson *et al.*, 1973; Toister and Loyter, 1973). Figure 11 shows data recalculated from Carlsson *et al.* (1973), summarizing the competition between reactivating chick erythrocyte nuclei, four different parameters being used to measure the

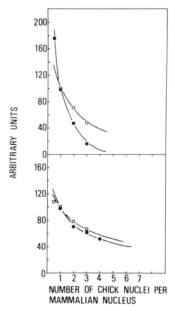

Fig. 11. Competition for rate-limiting factors in the reactivation of chick erythrocyte nuclei. The reactivation reaction was measured by the following parameters: ■——■, level of RNA polymerase activity in reactivated nuclei, as measured by the incorporation of ³H-labeled nucleoside triphosphate into acid-insoluble material; ○——○, level of RNA synthesis as measured by ³H uridine incorporation; □——□, nuclear diameter; ●——●, accumulation of mammalian nucleoplasmic antigen. The data were recalculated from Carlsson *et al.* (1973) using their 48-hour time point analysis carried out on rat epithelial cell × chick erythrocyte heterokaryons.

reactivation reaction. While the data shown cannot establish cause–effect relationships, it does show that rate-limiting factors for the reactivation reaction exist in the mammalian cell. Furthermore, it seems unlikely that ions or nucleotides would be rate-limiting factors since competition is observed also in an *in vitro* assay for endogenous RNA polymerase activity where the ionic environment is controlled and nucleotides are present in excess (Carlsson *et al.*, 1973).

Experiments have been carried out to determine whether the rate-limiting factors discussed above are localized in the mammalian cell nucleus or in the cytoplasm. For these experiments the reactivation reaction was carried out by fusing chick erythrocytes into enucleated mammalian cells. Figures 12 and 13 show that chick erythrocyte nuclei can undergo reactivation in the absence of the mammalian nucleus as judged here by morphology, but also as judged by specific mammalian protein accumulation, nucleic acid synthesis, and the appearance of new chick antigens (Ege *et al.*, 1973, 1975). Thus while mammalian to chick nucleus transfer of macromolecules may occur, it is not a *prerequisite* that macromolecules accumulating in the chick nucleus originate from the mammalian nucleus. The mammalian cytoplasm contains a pool of macromolecules (and/or the machinery to synthesize them), which can accumulate directly into reactivating chick erythrocyte nuclei. This conclusion is con-

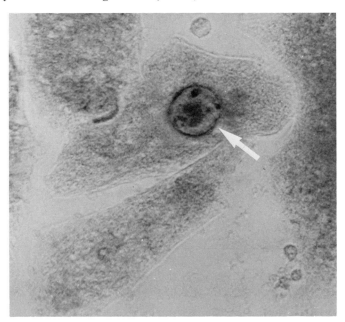

FIG. 12. Reactivation of chick erythrocyte nucleus (arrow) in an enucleate cell. Photograph was taken using a UV microscope. From Ege *et al.* (1975).

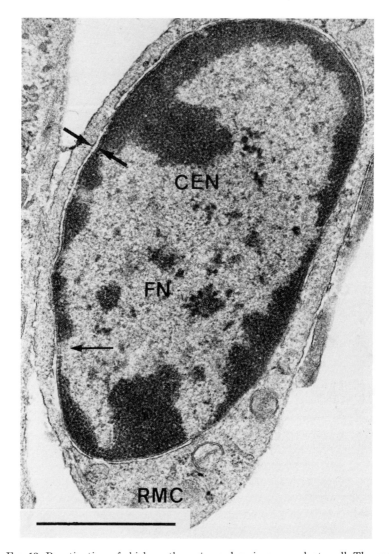

Fig. 13. Reactivation of chick erythrocyte nucleus in an enucleate cell. The reconstituted cell shown was obtained by fusion between a chick erythrocyte and a rat myoblast enucleated before fusion. The chick erythrocyte nucleus CEN exhibits a fragmented nucleolus FN. The nucleus is inserted within a rat myoblast cytoplasm RMC. It is surrounded by a nuclear envelope (two arrows) with nuclear pores (arrow). ×38,000. Scale shown represents 1 μm. From Dupuy-Coin *et al.* (1975).

sistent with that from pulse-chase experiments in heterokaryons (discussed in Section V, B), suggesting that nuclear protein synthesis is not closely linked to the deposition of the respective proteins in nuclei.

C. UNCOUPLING REACTIONS

A major advantage in the overall system described here for the analysis of controls operating on eukaryote chromosomal material is that the chick erythrocyte nucleus can be "operated on" without damaging the mammalian host cell. Changes in the reactivation reaction observed can then be *specifically* related to alterations which were made to the respective chick erythrocyte nucleus. Unfortunately, this advantage has not been fully exploited to date, and the experiments described below are hopefully a start to a useful area of research.

To try to distinguish between whether protein accumulation or new transcription of the chick DNA were primary events in the reactivation reaction, the effect of UV-irradiating chick erythrocytes *before* fusion has been analyzed (Harris, 1967; Bolund et al., 1969a; Appels et al., 1974a). The essential features of UV-irradiated chick erythrocytes are that (1) the virus receptors remain apparently unaffected because the erythrocytes can be fused into mammalian cells, (2) the DNA is sufficiently damaged to reduce its post-fusion capacity for RNA synthesis to 1–10% of what it was before. The results of analyses on the reactivation reaction within UV-irradiated chick erythrocyte nuclei show that large reductions in the transcription from chick DNA do *not* affect the protein accumulation and structural changes normally occurring during reactivation. This result, together with the very early accumulation of protein, argues for this phenomenon being a very early, perhaps the first, event in the reactivation reaction. The interpretation is consistent with current notions that nonhistone protein is somehow responsible for controlling DNA transcription (Stellwagen and Cole, 1969; Baserga, 1974).

A prediction from the model favored above is that inhibition of protein accumulation should have pleiotropic effects and inhibit other parameters of the reactivation reaction. Preliminary experiments along this line have been carried out by Darzynkiewicz et al. (1974) on the assumption that among the protein accumulating is an essential protease. Specific inhibitors of proteolytic enzymes administered to HeLa × chick erythrocyte heterokaryons post fusion were found to inhibit the reactivation reaction, as measured by morphology and transcription of chick DNA. While these data are consistent with a view that the action of a protease of the type found in mammalian nuclei (Furlan et al., 1968; Bartley and Chalkley, 1970; Garrels et al., 1972; Broström and Jeffay, 1972) is required for the reactivation reaction, the interpretation is not simple. Inhibitors such as N-α-tosyl-L-lysylchloromethane (TLCK) can block cells in a premitotic stage of the cell cycle (Collard and Smets, 1974), which would thus indirectly inhibit the reactivation of at least those nuclei which would have been reactivated in the postmitotic stage of heterokaryon divisions (see earlier discussion of Fig. 5). A less ambiguous experiment would be to render chick erythrocyte nuclei unsuitable templates for nuclear proteases *before* fusion (perhaps by pretreating erythrocytes with the trypsin inhibitor TLCK).

After some protein accumulation, structural changes, and transcription of the chick DNA have occurred, replication of the chick DNA can start. The early stages of the reactivation appear to be necessary for DNA synthesis to start, and in addition some specific mammalian factors present only in S phase cells are required. Evidence for the latter comes from observations showing that DNA synthesis occurred only in chick erythrocyte nuclei of increased size (and where chromatin decondensation had occurred) when these nuclei were found in S phase mammalian cells (Johnson and Harris, 1969).

At advanced stages of reactivation a visible nucleolus develops in chick erytrocyte nuclei. This has been shown to be required before the final step of the reactivation can occur, namely, the expression of a chick phenotype. To demonstrate this Harris and co-workers (Deák *et al.*, 1972; Deák, 1973) utilized UV-microbeam irradiation of individual nucleoli in reactivating chick erythrocyte nuclei. Irradiation of chick nucleoli after they developed as visible entities specifically prevented the appearance of chick phenotypic markers. Irradiation of nucleoplasm, as a control, did not elicit this response. These data thus indicated that the function of certain factors which became concentrated at the nucleolus when it developed as a visible entity were somehow necessary for subsequent expression of chick genes.

VIII. Conclusions

When a chick erythrocyte nucleus is introduced by cell fusion into the cytoplasm of a mammalian cell, we suggest that the first event is a redistribution of the cellular pool of mammalian nuclear protein. (Because of their small size and because they frequently lyse before fusion, the chick erythrocytes contribute very little cytoplasm to the heterokaryon.) Evidence suggests that the synthesis of nuclear protein is not closely linked to their deposition within the nucleus; this means that the above redistribution may occur mainly on the basis of a high affinity of normal nuclear proteins for sites within a nucleus. Such a redistribution would lead to a net accumulation of protein in the chick erythrocyte nucleus as this has an initially low total protein:DNA ratio. Structural changes in the chick chromatin may then occur as a result of an unknown action of low molecular weight (MW $< 60,000$) nonhistone polypeptides as well as other proteins not detected by present analyses and/or the action of a specific nuclear protease.

The group of proteins of molecular weight approximately 50,000 appear of particular interest here because during avian erythropoiesis these proteins are lost from the nucleus whereas in the reactivation they are among the first to reappear (see previous discussion, Section V, B). A specific nuclear protease may be responsible for the removal of chick erythrocyte-specific f2c as mammalian f1 histone accumulates in the chick chromatin—the overall reaction here would be analogous to the turnover of the f1 group of histones which may be required for an active, nonreplicative form of eukaryote chromatin (Stellwagen and Cole, 1969; Gurley and Hardin, 1970; Appels and Wells, 1972). An additional reaction could be the dephosphorylation of histone as suggested by Bradbury *et al.* (1974) to function either in the way suggested by these authors or by forming active sites for a protease. While dephosphorylation of some chromosomal sites may be of importance, phosphorylation of other sites may also be necessary for the reactivation reaction since in studies on avian erythropoiesis phosphorylation of chromosomal proteins has been correlated with an active state of the chromatin (Gershey and Kleinsmith, 1969; Seligy *et al.*, 1973; Brasch *et al.*, 1974). Other chemical modification reactions, such as acetylation, may also be of importance again as judged from studies on avian erythropoiesis (Allfrey, 1970). In general it seems likely that certain nuclear proteins will require the presence of other nuclear proteins within the chromatin before they can function, as shown in other systems of nucleic acid–protein interactions (Kurland, 1972; Huang and Buchanan, 1974). In this way the changes in the reactivating chick erythrocyte nucleus may reflect an ordered self-assembly process.

Soon after some structural changes have occurred in the chick chromatin it can be envisaged that the chick RNA polymerases already present, and possibly also mammalian RNA polymerases (among the protein accumulating) both begin transcribing the chick DNA. The sites of transcription for the RNA polymerase may be modulated either by the incoming mammalian proteins, by chick proteins already present in the chick erythrocyte nuclei and by losses of specific chick proteins. The RNA synthesized remains within the nucleus until a nucleolus develops in the reactivated chick erythrocyte nucleus. The transport of RNA to the cytoplasm is then closely correlated with nucleolar development. After transport the chick RNA appears to be available to mammalian ribosomes for translation into identifiable chick gene products. If the reactivated chick erythrocyte nucleus is in an S phase mammalian cells, DNA synthesis is frequently initiated in the chick nucleus.

The overall result of the reactivation of chick erythrocyte nuclei in mammalian tissue culture cells is that the chick nucleus acquires a broad spectrum of mammalian proteins because at the early stages of reactivation the mammalian nucleus is the only one specifying synthesis of nuclear proteins in the heterokaryon. Information about the nature of proteins accumulating in reactivating chick erythrocyte nuclei has been obtained, but it is not yet possible to state their exact role in the reactivation reaction. It seems likely, however, as discussed speculatively above, that among the mammalian nucleospecific proteins that do accumulate there are some which should be considered as "signals" of direct regulatory importance. Further analysis of the reactivation reaction should lead to an identification of such signals.

REFERENCES

Allfrey, V. G. (1970). *Fed. Proc., Fed. Amer. Soc. Exp. Biol.* **29**, 1447–1460.

Appels, R., and Ringertz, N. R. (1974). *Cell Differentiation* **3**, 1–7.

Appels, R., and Wells, J. R. E. (1972). *J. Mol. Biol.* **70**, 425–434.

Appels, R., Harlow, R., Tolstoshev, P., and Wells, J. R. E. (1973). *In* "The Biochemistry of Gene Expression in Higher Trganisms" (J. K. Pollack and J. W. Lee, eds.), pp. 191–205. Australian and New Zealand Book Co., Sydney.

Appels, R., Bolund, L., Goto, S., and Ringertz, N. R. (1974a). *Exp. Cell Res.* **85**, 182–190.

Appels, R., Bolund, L., and Ringertz, N. R. (1974b). *J. Mol. Biol.* **87**, 339–356.

Appels, R., Bell, P., and Ringertz, N. R. (1975a). *Exp. Cell Res.* **92**, 79–86.

Appels, R., Tallroth, E., Appels, D. M., and Ringertz, N. R. (1975b). *Exp. Cell Res.* **92**, 70–78.

Attardi, G., Parnas, H., Hwang, H.-I., and Attardi, B. (1966). *J. Mol. Biol.* **20**, 145–182.

Barker, K. L. (1971). *Biochemistry* **10**, 284–291.

Bartley, J., and Chalkley, R. (1970). *J. Biol. Chem.* **245**, 4286–4292.

Baserga, R. (1974). *Life Sci.* **15**, 1057–1072.

Bolund, L., Darzynkiewicz, Z., and Ringertz, N. R. (1969a). *Exp. Cell Res.* **56**, 406–410.

Bolund, L., Ringertz, N. R., and Harris, H. (1969b). *J. Cell Sci.* **4**, 71–87.

Boyd, Y. L., and Harris, H. (1973). *J. Cell Sci.* **13**, 841–861.

Bradbury, E. M., Inglis, R. J., and Matthews, H. R. (1974). *Nature (London)* **247**, 257–261.

Brasch, K., Adams, G. H. M., and Neelin, J. M. (1974). *J. Cell Sci.* **15**, 659–669.

Broström, C. O., and Jeffay, H. (1972). *Biochim. Biophys. Acta* **278**, 15–27.

Bustin, M., and Stollar, B. D. (1973). *J. Biol. Chem.* **248**, 3506–3510.

Carlsson, S.-A., Moore, G. P. M., and Ringertz, N. R. (1973). *Exp. Cell Res.* **76**, 234–241.

Carlsson, S.-A., Luger, O., Ringertz, N. R., and Savage, R. E. (1974a). *Exp. Cell Res.* **84**, 47–55.

Carlsson, S.-A., Ringertz, N. R., and Savage, R. E. (1974b). *Exp. Cell Res.* **84**, 255–266.

Choe, B.-K., and Rose, N. R. (1974). *Exp. Cell Res.* **83**, 261–270.

Clemens, G. B. (1972). Ph.d. Thesis, University of Glasgow, Scotland.

Collard, J. G., and Smets, L. A. (1974). *Exp. Cell Res.* **86**, 75–80.

Cramer, J. H., Sebastian, J., Rownd, R. H., and Halvorson, H. O. (1974). *Proc. Nat. Acad. Sci. U.S.* **71**, 2188–2192.

Darzynkiewicz, Z., and Chelmicka-Szorc, E. (1972). *Exp. Cell Res.* **74**, 131–139.
Darzynkiewicz, Z., Chelmicka-Szorc, E., and Arnason, B. G. W. (1974). *Proc. Nat. Acad. Sci. U.S.* **71**, 644–647.
Deák, I. (1973). *J. Cell Sci.* **13**, 395–401.
Deák, I., Sidebottom, E., and Harris, H. (1972). *J. Cell Sci.* **11**, 379–391.
Deitsch, A. (1955). *Lab. Invest.* **4**, 324–351.
Dendy, P. R., and Harris, H. (1973). *J. Cell Sci.* **12**, 831–837.
Dingman, C. W., and Sporn, M. B. (1964). *J. Biol. Chem.* **239**, 3483–3492.
Dupuy-Coin, A.-M., Ege, T., Bouteille, M., and Ringertz, N. R. (1975). *Exp. Cell Res.* (in press).
Ege, T., Zeuthen, J., and Ringertz, N. R. (1973). *In* "Chromosome Identification" (T. Caspersson and L. Zech, eds.), Nobel Symp. No. 23, pp. 189–194. Academic Press, New York.
Ege, T., Zeuthen, J., and Ringertz, N. R. (1975). *Somatic Cell Genet.* **1**, 65–80.
Elgin, S. C. R., and Bonner, J. (1970). *Biochemistry* **9**, 4440–4447.
Franke, W. W., Deumling, B., Ermen, B., Jarasch, E.-D., and Kleinig, H. (1970). *J. Cell Biol.* **46**, 379–395.
Furlan, M., Jericijo, M., and Suhar, A. (1968). *Biochim. Biophys. Acta* **167**, 154–160.
Garrels, J. I., Elgin, S. C. R., and Bonner, T. (1972). *Biochem. Biophys. Res. Commun.* **46**, 545–551.
Gershey, E. L., and Kleinsmith, L. J. (1969). *Biochim. Biophys. Acta* **194**, 519–525.
Gledhill, B. L., Gledhill, M. P., Rigler, R., Jr., and Ringertz, N. R. (1966). *Exp. Cell Res.* **41**, 652–665.
Goto, S., and Ringertz, N. R. (1974). *Exp. Cell Res.* **85**, 173–181.
Gurley, L. R., and Hardin, J. M. (1970). *Arch. Biochem. Biophys.* **136**, 392–399.
Harlow, R., Tolstoshev, P., and Wells, J. R. E. (1972). *Cell Differentiation* **2**, 341–349.
Harris, H. (1965). *Nature (London)* **206**, 583–588.
Harris, H. (1967). *J. Cell Sci.* **2**, 23–32.
Harris, H., and Cook, P. R. (1969). *J. Cell Sci.* **5**, 121–133.
Harris, H., Sidebottom, E., Grace, D. M., and Bramwell, M. E. (1969). *J. Cell Sci.* **4**, 499–525.
Hilder, V. A., and MacLean, N. (1974). *J. Cell Sci.* **16**, 133–142.
Huang, W. M., and Buchanan, J. M. (1974). *Proc. Nat. Acad. Sci. U.S.* **71**, 2226–2230.
Johnson, R. T., and Harris, H. (1969). *J. Cell Sci.* **5**, 625–644.
Johnson, R. T., Rao, P. N., and Hughes, H. D. (1970). *J. Cell. Physiol.* **76**, 151–158.
Kao, F. T. (1973). *Proc. Nat. Acad. Sci. U.S.* **70**, 2893–2898.
Kernell, A.-M., Bolund, L., and Ringertz, N. R (1971). *Exp. Cell Res.* **65**, 1–6.
Kleinig, H., Zentgraf, H., Comes, P., and Stadler, J. (1971). *J. Biol. Chem.* **246**, 2996–3000.
Klinger, H. P., and Shin, S.-I. (1974). *Proc. Nat. Acad. Sci. U.S.* **71**, 1398–1402.
Kurland, C. G. (1972). *Annu. Rev. Biochem.* **41**, 377–408.
Leake, R. E., Trench, M. E., and Barry, J. M. (1972). *Exp. Cell Res.* **71**, 17–26.
Leeman, U., and Ruch, F. (1972). *J. Histochem. Cytochem.* **20**, 659–671.
Le Stourgeon, W. M., Nations, C., and Rusch, H. P. (1973). *Arch. Biochem. Biophys* **159**, 861–872.
Levy, N. L., Snyderman, R., Ladda, R. L., and Liberman, R. (1973). *Proc. Nat. Acad. Sci. U.S.* **70**, 3125–3129.
Lindberg, L. G. (1974). *Acta Pathol. Microbiol. Scand.* **82**, 299–310.
MacGillivray, A. J., Cameron, A., Karuze, R. J., Richwood, D., and Paul, J. (1972). *Biochim. Biophys. Acta* **277**, 384–402.

Moore, G. P. M., and Ringertz, N. R. (1973). *Exp. Cell Res.* **76**, 223–228.

Prescott, D. M., and Goldstein, L. (1968). *J. Cell Biol.* **39**, 404–414.

Reeder, R. H., and Roeder, R. G. (1972). *J. Mol. Biol.* **67**, 433–441.

Richards, B. M., and Bajer, A. (1961). *Exp. Cell Res.* **22**, 503–508.

Rickwood, D., Riches, P. G., and MacGillivray, A. J. (1973). *Biochim. Biophys. Acta* **299**, 162–197.

Rigler, R., Killander, D., Bolund, L., and Ringertz, N. R. (1969). *Exp. Cell Res.* **55**, 215–224.

Ringertz, N. R. (1969). *In* "Handbook of Molecular Cytology" (A. Lima-de-Faria, ed.), pp. 656–684. North-Holland Publ., Amsterdam.

Ringertz, N. R., and Bolund, L. (1974a). *Int. Rev. Exp. Pathol.* **13**, 83–116.

Ringertz, N. R., and Bolund, L. (1974b). *In* "The Cell Nucleus" (H. Busch, ed.), Vol. 3, 417–446.

Ringertz, N. R., and Savage, R. E. (1975). "Cell Hybrids." Academic Press, New York.

Ringertz, N. R., Carlsson, S.-A., Ege, T., and Bolund, L. (1971). *Proc. Nat. Acad. Sci. U.S.* **68**, 3228–3232.

Rosenqvist, M., Stenman, S., and Ringertz, N. R., (1975). *Exp. Cell Res.* **92**, 515–518.

Rosselet, A., and Ruch, F. (1968). *J. Histochem. Cytochem.* **16**, 459–466.

Rovera, N. B., and Baserga, R. (1971). *J. Cell. Physiol.* **77**, 201–212.

Ruddon, R. W., and Rainey, C. H. (1970). *Biochem. Biophys. Res. Commun.* **40**, 152–160.

Schechter, N. M. (1973). *Biochim. Biophys. Acta* **308**, 129–136.

Scherrer, K., Marcaud, L., Zajdela, F., London, I. M., and Gros, F. (1966). *Proc. Nat. Acad. Sci. U.S.* **56**, 1571–1578.

Schneeberger, E. E., and Harris, H. (1966). *J. Cell Sci.* **1**, 401–406.

Schwartz, A. G., Cook, P. R., and Harris, H. (1971). *Nature (London)* **230**, 5–8.

Seligy, V. L., Adams, G. H. M., and Neelin, J. M. (1973). *In* "The Biochemistry of Gene Expression in Higher Organisms" (J. K. Pollack and J. W. Lee, eds.), pp. 177–190. Australian and New Zealand Book Co., Sydney.

Shelton, K. R., and Allfrey, V. G. (1970). *Nature (London)* **228**, 132–134.

Shelton, K. R., and Neelin, J. M. (1971). *Biochemistry* **10**, 2342–2348.

Sidebottom, E., and Harris, H. (1969). *J. Cell Sci.* **5**, 351–364.

Small, J. V., and Davies, H. G. (1970). *J. Cell Sci.* **7**, 15–33.

Sotirov, N., and Johns, E. W. (1972). *J. Immunol.* **109**, 686–691.

Spelsberg, T. C., Mitchell, W. M., Chytil, F., Wilson, E. M., and O'Malley, B. W. (1973). *Biochim. Biophys. Acta.* **312**, 765–778.

Stedman, E., and Stedman, E. (1950). *Nature (London)* **166**, 780–781.

Stellwagen, R. H., and Cole, R. D. (1969). *Ann. Rev. Biochem.* **38**, 951–990.

Teng, C. S., and Hamilton, T. H. (1969). *Proc. Nat. Acad. Sci. U.S.* **63**, 465–472.

Tengk, C. S., Teng, C. T., and Allfrey, V. G. (1971). *J. Biol. Chem.* **246**, 3597–3609.

Thompson, L. R., and McCarthy, B. J. (1968). *Biochem. Biophys. Res. Commun.* **30**, 166–172.

Toister, Z., and Loyter, A. (1973). *J. Biol. Chem.* **248**, 422–432.

Tsuboi, A., and Baserga, R. (1972). *J. Cell. Physiol.* **80**, 107–117.

Williams, A. F. (1972). *J. Cell Sci.* **10**, 27–46.

Zakai, N., Loyter, A., and Kulka, R. G. (1974). *J. Cell Biol.* **61**, 241–248.

Zentgraf, H., Deumling, B. I., Jarasch, E.-D., and Franke, W. W. (1971). *J. Biol. Chem.* **246**, 2986–2995.

Zylber, E. A., and Penman, S. (1971). *Proc. Nat. Acad. Sci. U.S.* **68**, 2861–2865.

CHAPTER 6

Drosophila ANTIGENS: THEIR SPATIAL AND TEMPORAL DISTRIBUTION, THEIR FUNCTION AND CONTROL

David B. Roberts

GENETICS LABORATORY
BIOCHEMISTRY DEPARTMENT
OXFORD UNIVERSITY
OXFORD, ENGLAND

I. Introduction

Development is best understood, at the present time, in terms of the theory of variable gene activity. A gene is activated to produce mRNA. This is translated into proteins, and these molecules in their turn govern the structure and function of the cell. Changes in these proteins will lead to change in structure and function, in other words to development. In *Drosophila* much is known about gene activity from the studies of chromosome puffs (Ashburner, 1972; Berendes, 1972); much is known about the control of this gene activity by hormones (Ashburner, 1972; Berendes, 1972; Doane, 1973) and about the changes that occur in cells and tissues during development (Sonnenblick, 1950; Poulson, 1950; Bodenstein, 1950). Little, however, is known about alterations in the molecular composition of the cells, which is the response to changing gene activity.

The aim of these studies has been to examine the protein molecules of different types of cells at different stages of development, to investigate the role played by these molecules in the changes that occur during development, and to study the control of the synthesis of these molecules. These investigations have been carried out using immunological techniques. The results are sufficiently encouraging to suggest that this approach to the study of these problems in *Drosophila*, or in other organisms, is worthwhile and fulfills, at least in part, the conviction of Brachet (1960) ". . . there is also no doubt that the use of immunological methods—which are constantly being refined—will lead us a long way towards the ultimate goal: the understanding of the biochemical mechanisms of tissue and cell differentiation."

II. Experimental Approach to the Analysis of Antigens

A. IMMUNODIFFUSION

In its simplest terms, the problem that confronts us is this: we have two mixtures of soluble antigens, an extract of *Drosophila* larvae and an extract of *Drosophila* flies, and we want to know which antigens are common to both extracts and which are not. Two techniques have been used to resolve this problem, the double-diffusion plate and the immunoelectrophoresis plate. A diagram of a double-diffusion plate and its interpretation are shown in Fig. 1. The advantage of the double-diffusion plate is that it permits both quantitative and qualitative comparisons of extracts and there is no ambiguity over these comparisons because the precipitin bands either show continuity between the two extracts, indicating presence in both, although perhaps at different concentrations, or no continuity, in which case the antigen is missing from one extract. The disadvantage of double-diffusion plates is that when many precipitin reactions are being studied simultaneously they become superimposed and the resolution is poor.

A diagram of an immunoelectrophoresis plate and its interpretation are shown in Fig. 2. The advantage of the immunoelectrophoresis plate is that it gives much better resolution; far more antibody–antigen reactions can be studied. The disadvantages of this technique are that it re-

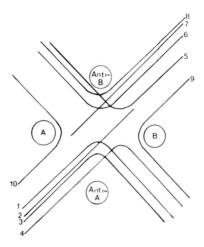

FIG. 1a. A and B are mixtures of antigens. Anti-A and anti-B are rabbit antisera produced against A and B, respectively. The ten antibody–antigen precipitin bands are interpreted as follows: 1, 3, 6 and 8 are present in A and B at the same relative concentrations; 4 and 5 are present in A and B, but more concentrated in A because the band is closer to the antibody well; 2 is present only in A, and 7 in B; 9 and 10 are present in B and A, respectively; antibodies against both are present in anti-A and anti-B.

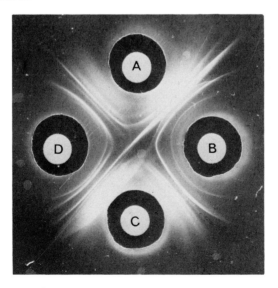

FIG. 1b. A, Anti-embryo extract; B, embryo extract; C, anti-third-instar larval extract; D, third-instar larval extract. Plate was stained with Amido schwarz 10B.

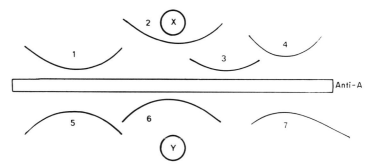

FIG. 2a. X and Y are complex mixtures of antigens. Anti-A is a rabbit antiserum prepared against a third antigen A. The seven precipitin arcs indicated are interpreted as follows: 1 and 5 are negatively charged antigens, because the apex of both arcs has migrated the same distance from the origin and because the arcs are the same shape, indicating the same distribution of charged molecules. Arcs 1 and 5 would, in these studies, be considered to be the same antigen in X and Y. For similar reasons, arcs 2 and 6 would be considered the same although 6 would be relatively more concentrated because it is closer to the antibody slot. Arc 3 is an antigen in X but not in Y. Arcs 4 and 7 present a difficult problem. From the apex of the two arcs they have migrated the same distance from the origin, but the shapes of the two arcs are quite different; arc 4 consists of molecules all with the same charge, and arc 7 consists of some molecules with a high positive charge and more molecules with a lesser positive charge, although all molecules carry the same antigenic determinants. In these studies, because of the heterogeneity of arc 7, arcs 4 and 7 would be considered to be different antigens; such examples are rare.

FIG. 2b. A, third-instar larval extract; B, second-instar larval extract; C, anti-larval serum.

quires a subjective interpretation of the identity or otherwise of two antigens, and it does not permit the easy, unambiguous, demonstration of changes in relative antigen concentrations.

The basic strategy of the studies was, by means of these techniques, to immunize rabbits with the different extracts and to compare every pair of extracts with every antiserum and every pair of antisera with every extract. In practice this required very many plates, and so not all pairwise comparisons were made. By comparing sets of plates run at the same time and under the same conditions, the number of plates set up was reduced. Nevertheless hundreds of plates were examined.

The same antigen was detected by many antisera and the same antibody reacted with many different extracts, and so there were continual cross checks on the interpretation of the results. Because of these many cross checks it is unlikely that, even in view of the subjective analysis of immunoelectrophoresis plates, there are many errors of interpretation.

B. Protein Nature of Antigens

The main interest in these studies has been in protein antigens. Most, if not all, of the antigens we studied were proteins. This was established by incubating extracts with Pronase and studying the loss of antigens. Not all extracts were examined in this way, so that some of the antigens may not have been proteins, but all the extracts that were examined revealed only antigens affected by Pronase. For simplicity I will write about proteins in the remainder of this paper.

C. Immunodiffusion vs Electrophoresis

The more common technique for resolving the proteins in a complex mixture of proteins is electrophoresis, and this technique has been used successfully to resolve proteins in extracts of *Drosophila*. The immunoelectrophoresis technique does have the advantage of separating the proteins in two dimensions, giving better resolution. Patel and Schneiderman (1969) made a comparison of electrophoretic and immunoelectrophoretic analyses of *Hyalophora cecropia* hemolymph and demonstrated that proteins were revealed by the immunoelectrophoric technique that were hidden in the electrophoretic one. There are many techniques for the two-dimensional electrophoresis of proteins, but these are more difficult than immunoelectrophoresis and are not readily adapted to a large-scale survey.

Where it has been possible to make a comparison between electrophoretic techniques and our own studies (Pasteur and Kastritis, 1971), the present studies detect at least as many proteins.

D. Disadvantages of Immunodiffusion and Electrophoresis

There are two major disadvantages of both the immunological technique and the electrophoretic technique for analyzing proteins. Both fail to analyze insoluble proteins. This can be overcome in part by solubilizing the proteins with detergents. The second objection is more serious:

neither technique can demonstrate the absence of a protein, only that it is at a concentration too low to be detected. Because of this all analyses may be quantitative. This possibility is underlined by the observation of Bishop (Bishop *et al.*, 1974) that there are 4000 different species of mRNA in cultured *Drosphila* cells. This can be interpreted, if the estimate of 5000 genes for *Drosophila* (Judd *et al.*, 1972) is correct, as meaning that all genes are active at a low constitutive level; this would, without posttranscriptional control, result in a low level of synthesis of all proteins. For simplicity in these studies, a protein detected in one extract, but not in a second extract with the same protein concentration, is considered to be missing from the second extract.

III. Antigens of *Drosophila* Developmental Stages, Tissues, and Cells

A. PREPARATION OF ANTISERA

Using these simple immunological techniques, we have carried out three series of experiments. In the first (Roberts, 1971), using antisera prepared against extracts from different developmental stages, we studied the distribution of antigens in different developmental stages. In the second series (Boavida, 1973; Boavida and Roberts, 1975), we prepared antisera against extracts of six different tissues from third-instar larvae and used these antisera to study the distribution of the antigens in the tissues. In the final series of experiments (Moir, 1974; Moir and Roberts 1975), antisera were prepared against extracts of two *Drosophila* cell lines. These antisera together with those against tissues and developmental stages were used to study the distribution of antigens in ten cell lines and at six developmental stages. Because the same antisera were used, it was possible to identify the antigens found in the second series of experiments with those found in the third series, so that seven of the nine possible studies shown in Table I were carried out. The results are given in Table II.

TABLE I

POSSIBLE ANTIGEN STUDIES

Antibody	Developmental stages	Tissues	Cells
Developmental stages	+		+
Tissues	+	+	+
Cells	+		+

TABLE II

RESULTS OF ANTIGEN STUDIES[a,b]

Source of extract	Group A	Group B
Egg	xxxxxxxxxxxxxxxxxxxxxxxxx	xxxxxxxxxxxxxxxxxxxxxx
Embryo	xxxxxxxxxxxxxxxxxxxxxxxxx	xxxxxxxxxxxxxxxxxxxxxx
1st	xxxxxxxxxxxx	xxxxxxxxxxxxxxxxxxxxxx
2nd	xxxxxxxxxxxx xxxxxxxxxxxxxxxxx x	xxxxxxxxxxxxxxxxxxxxxx
3rd	xxxxxxxxxxxxxxxxxxxxxxxxxxxx xxx	xxxxxxxxxxxxxxxxxxxxxx
Fly	xxxxxxxxxxxxxxxxx xxxxx	xxxxxxxxxxxxxxxxxxxxxx
L1	xx xxxx xxxxxx x x xx x	xxxxxxxxxxxxxxxxxxxxxx
L2	xx xxxx xxxxx xxx x x x x	xxxxxxxxxxxxxxxxxxxxxx
L3	xx x xx xxxxxx xxxxx x x xx	xxxxxxxxxxxxxxxxxxxxxx
Gm1	xx xxxx xxx x xxxx xx x xxxx	xxxxxxxxxxxxxxxxxxxxxx
Gm2	xx xx xxx x xxxxx x x xxx x	xxxxxxxxxxxxxxxxxxxxxx
Gm3	xx xxxx xxx x xxxxx x x xxxxx	xxxxxxxxxxxxxxxxxxxxxxxxxx
K100	xx xxxx xxxx x x xxx xx xx xx x	xxxxxxxxxxxxxxxxxxxxxx
K96	xx xxx xxxx x x xx x x xx	xxxxxxxxxxxxxxxxxxxxxx
K85	xx xxx xxxx x xx x x x	xxxxxxxxxxxxxxxxxxxxxx
K84	xx xxx xxxx x xx x x x	xxxxxxxxxxxxxxxxxxxxxx
FB	x xx x xx xx x x xxxx xx x	x xxxxxxx xxxx xxx xx x
ID	xx x x xx x x x	x xxxxxxxxxx xx xxxxx
SG	x x x x x x	x xxxxxxxxx xx xxxx
MT	x x x xxx xx x xxxx xx x xx x	xxxx xxxx xxx xx xxxx
HC	xx xx x xxxxx	xx x xx x

[a] From Moir (1974).

[b] x shows the presence of the antigen in the extract indicated. Group A antigens are "organism" antigens (luxury) and group B antigens are "cell" antigens (essential) (see text). The L lines were a gift from Dr. I. Schneider (Schneider, 1972); the Gm lines were a gift from Dr. S. Dolfini (Mosna and Dolfini, 1972). The cloned line K100 and the subclones of that clone, K96, K85, K84, were gifts from Dr. G. Echalier (Echalier and Ohanessian, 1970).

B. Developmental Stage Antigens

From the results in Table II it can be seen that during the development of *Drosophila* there is a changing pattern of proteins in the organism. This reflects the changing pattern of gene activity—ignoring post-transcriptional control—although it must be remembered that genes will be active before proteins are detected and proteins will be detected after genes have ceased to be active.

While each developmental stage is characterized by a unique protein pattern it is important to consider quantitative changes. Throughout all these studies, quantitative changes were obvious. The relative concentration of a protein frequently changed dramatically from one developmental stage to another or from one tissue to another while the relative concentration of the same protein in different extractions of the same developmental stage or tissue remained constant. Obviously, not only what proteins are present but at what concentration is important for the development of the organism or for determining the structure and function of a cell. The analysis of quantitative differences is difficult and, while the more easily analyzed qualitative difference remain to be studied, our efforts have been concentrated on these. But at no time should the significance of the quantitative changes be minimized.

C. Tissue Antigens

A study of the tissues shows each to be characterized by a unique pattern of proteins although few tissue-unique proteins were found; thus the pattern of proteins seems to be more critical than unique proteins. A statistical analysis of the antigen patterns of each pair of tissues showed that imaginal discs and salivary glands were significantly similar at the 0.1% level. No other pair of tissues showed such similarity. This result supports the suggestion (Ashburner, 1970a) that salivary glands synthesize proteins subsequently sequestered by the imaginal discs.

D. Cell Line Antigens

Each cell line shows a unique pattern of antigens reflecting their unique properties (morphology, karyotype, response to hormones, etc.) In order to suggest a tissue origin for the cell lines, we compared the antigen pattern of each with that of each tissue. All cell lines possessed patterns significantly similar to imaginal discs and salivary glands at the 0.5% level. While these studies cannot distinguish between an imaginal disc and a salivary gland origin for the cell lines, the evidence suggests that all cell lines, whether prepared from early embryos (Gm and K) or late embryos (L) are derived from the primordia of one or other of these tissues.

The clone and subclones, while similar in their antigen patterns, do show differences. These differences either reflect adversely on the cloning technique or more likely indicate changes in the cells after cloning. If such obvious changes are detected when so few proteins are analyzed it suggests that after a number of generations cloned cells may be very heterogeneous and that this heterogeneity must be taken into consideration when interpreting the results of experiments using these clones.

These results fulfill the expectations of most developmental biologists, that the development of an organism is accompanied by a changing pattern of proteins (both quantitative and qualitative), which reflects differential gene activity, and that the different cell types are associated with different patterns of proteins, again reflecting differential gene activity.

IV. Role Played by Proteins in Development

A. Essential and Luxury Proteins

The first suggestion as to the role played by these proteins in development comes from studying their distribution both throughout development and in different tissues and cell types. Some authors (Holtzer and Abbot, 1968; Ephrussi, 1972) have found it convenient to consider two classes of cellular proteins: "essential molecules," or "household items," which are necessary for the viability of cells; and "luxury molecules," which are "responsible for the state of differentiation of the cell." In more genetic terms we can consider essential molecules to be the protein products of genes that mutate to give cell autonomous lethals (Ripoll and Garcia-Bellido, 1973) whereas luxury molecules would be the protein products of genes that mutate to give non-cell autonomous lethals.

These arguments are, of course, oversimplifications, since it is the function rather than the protein which is essential. Two different cell types may achieve the same ends by different means, thus the means of achieving the end would be essential in one cell type and luxury in another. Isozymes, in the sense that the term is applied to lactate dehydrogenase, illustrate this point. In the heart the A4 homopolymer predominates whereas in the muscle the B4 molecule is the majority class. In the muscle B4 is essential and A4 probably luxury and in the heart vice versa. What is important is that both tissues have the essential function.

Notwithstanding these objections it is reasonable to suppose that most essential proteins will be found in all cells at all times while most luxury proteins will be found in limited cell types and at limited stages of development. A total of 85 proteins was detected and 23 of these (27%) were found at all developmental stages and in all cell lines and are probably essential proteins (Table II, Group B). They were not found in all tissues, as would be expected, because tissues were not analyzed with all antisera. Twenty-seven percent essential proteins may be an underestimate as essential proteins concerned with cell division may be at too low a concentration to be detected during the larval stage, when little cell division takes place, and essential functions carried out by different proteins in different cells (isozymes) would be overlooked.

Mutations affecting the genes for essential proteins would be homozygous lethal with the effective lethal phase early in development. The precise time of death would depend on the extent of maternal contribution to the egg of the essential protein. Studies of the effective lethal phase of lethal mutants (reviewed by Hadorn, 1961) given an average of 20% lethals dying early in development (egg or egg/larval boundary). This is in agreement with the present estimate of 27% essential proteins.

Judd et al. (1972) have suggested that *Drosophila* has 5000 structural genes. From the present studies about 30% of these would code for essential polypeptide chains. The remaining gene products would represent the polypeptide chains which make luxury proteins that are responsible for the differentiated state of the cell and polypeptide chains responsible for the control of gene activity. These controlling proteins would be at concentrations not detected in this study although they may be detected in an immunological study of *Drosophila* chromatin and chromosomal proteins (Andrews and Roberts, 1974; Roberts and Andrews, 1975). From these considerations of the distribution of the proteins we can suggest which are the essential proteins concerned with basic metabolic activity, etc., and are only likely to show quantitative changes and which proteins are likely to play a role in the development and differentiation of *Drosophila* and show qualitative changes which are suitable for the study of control processes.

The work "luxury" has unfortunate connotations for use in the present context and perhaps a more descriptive and less prejudiced terminology would be "cell proteins" for those proteins necessary for the viability of each and every cell and "organism proteins" for those proteins—excluding cell proteins—necessary for the normal development and behavior of the organism.

B. Enzyme Activity

To obtain a more precise knowledge of the function of these proteins immunoelectrophoresis plates were stained for enzyme activity. Many enzyme–antibody precipitates retain catalytic activity on double-diffusion plates (Roberts and Pateman, 1964). Using standard enzyme stains (Brewer, 1970), it was possible to attribute specific catalytic activities to specific precipitin arcs on immunoelectrophoresis plates with *Drosophila* extracts (Table III). Many arcs stained for enzyme activity, but only one of these (alcohol dehydrogenase) could be associated with an arc that was also stained by the less sensitive protein stain.

Many enzyme strains showed complex arcs suggesting multiple molec-

TABLE III

ASSOCIATION OF ACTIVITY IN EXTRACTS WITH PRECIPITIN ARCS ON PLATES

IUB E.C. number	Trivial name	Activity in extracts	Number of bands staining on plates	Previously reported activity in *Drosophila*
3.1.3.2	Acid phosphatase	P[a]	1	P
1.1.1.1	Alcohol dehydrogenase (NAD)	P	1	P
3.1.3.1	Alkaline phosphatase	—	—[b]	P
	Esterases	P	2	P
1.4.1.2	Glutamate dehydrogenase (NAD)	P	1	—
1.1.1.49	Glucose-6-phosphate dehydrogenase (NADP)	P	—	P
1.1.1.8	α-Glycerolphosphate dehydrogenase (NAD)	P	1	P
2.6.1.1	Glutamic–oxaloacetic transaminase	?	2	P
1.1.1.42	Isocitrate dehydrogenase (NADP)	P	1	P
1.1.1.27	Lactate dehydrogenase (NAD)	P	—	P
1.1.1.37	Malate dehydrogenase (NAD)	P	2	P
1.1.1.40	Malate dehydrogenase (NADP)	P	1	—
	Octanol dehydrogenase (NAD)	P	1	P
	Octanol dehydrogenase (NADP)	P	—	P
1.1.1.44	Phosphogluconate dehydrogenase (NADP)	P	—	P
	Xanthine dehydrogenase (NAD)	P	—	P

[a] Present.

[b] The lack of enzyme activity on plates when the enzyme is found in the extract is due either to no antibody being present to precipitate the enzyme or to the enzyme–antibody complex having no residual activity.

ular forms of the same enzyme, and in two cases, malate dehydrogenase and glutamic–oxalocetic transaminase, two immunologically distinct forms stained for the same enzyme activity (Fig. 3). These probably represent the cytoplasmic and mitochondrial forms of the same enzyme.

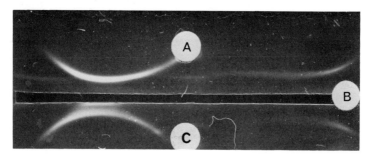

FIG. 3. Immunoelectrophoresis plate stained for malate dehydrogenase activity. A, fly extract; B, anti-egg; C, third-instar larval extract.

With the exception of alcohol dehydrogenase it was not possible to identify the function of any of the proteins found in these experiments. But, in order to study how these proteins influence the development and differentiation of *Drosophila*, it is not necessary, at this stage, to define their immediate biochemical functions. Instead we have exploited techniques, developed over many years by *Drosophila* geneticists, to study what happens to the development and differentiation of the organism when we take away a single protein.

V. Effect of Mutation on the Protein Pattern of Developing *Drosophila*

The protein pattern of *Drosophila* changes in a regular way during normal development. In a study of the significance of these changes, and perhaps the significance of single proteins, the protein pattern of developmental mutants was investigated. The only developmental mutants considered here are those in which development is completely upset—in other words, lethal mutants. The contribution made by studies of lethal mutants to developmental biology has been well reviewed by Hadorn (1961). The present studies are a continuation of the early studies on *Drosophila* lethals, with the addition of an immunological analysis to investigate molecular changes.

A. Selection of Mutants

While it is simple to select lethal mutants, there is a problem that must be overcome before any comparison can be made between the protein pattern of the mutant and that of the wild type. This problem, discussed by Wright (1970), is that lethal mutants must be maintained as heterozygotes. The homozygous lethals for these studies are obtained when the heterozygotes are crossed. Only one-fourth of the progeny will be the relevant homozygotes, and these must be distinguished from their sibs. We have overcome this problem in three ways: (1) by selecting late lethal mutants—mutants that die after their sibs have pupated; (2) by selecting lethals on the third chromosome marked with the recessive mutant *red;* the lethal homozygotes are distinguished from their sibs having red Malpighian tubules; (3) by selecting temperature-sensitive lethals; these are kept as homozygotes at the permissive temperature and studied at the restrictive temperature.

The experiments with late lethals were not wholly successful. It became apparent, when we were able to distinguish the homozygous lethal mutants from their nonmutant sibs in the experiment using *red*, that many nonmutants failed to pupate and survived a long time as larvae. The reason for this is unknown. These nonmutants were harvested together with the late lethal mutant larvae, and the wild-type proteins from these nonmutant larvae contaminated the extracts so that qualitative differences were obscured.

The study of temperature-sensitive mutants is incomplete. Flies homozygous for the recessive third chromosome marker *red* [for a description of the markers and balancers used, see Lindsley and Grell (1968)] were mutagenized, EMS being used as a mutagen, and lethal mutants were selected. Many of the lethal mutants died before the red Malpighian tubules could be detected in first-instar larvae, and so a further selection was made of lethals that survived until the red Malpighian tubules could be distinguished. Twenty-two lethals were selected (Table IV).

TABLE IV

THIRD CHROMOSOME LETHAL MUTANTS[a]

Mutant	Number
Early larval lethals (first or second instar)	4
Late larval lethals (third instar)	6
Larval/pupal lethals (dying as larvae or pupae)	11
Pupal lethals	1

[a] The temporal age at the time of death varied considerably. One of the late larval lethals survived more than 30 days. All the mutants survived at their terminal developmental stage longer than the wild type took to pass through that stage during normal development.

B. Immunological Analysis of Mutants

Extracts of the mutants were prepared from all ages at 24-hour intervals from 72 hours until death. These extracts were them compared on double diffusion plates with extracts of wild type of the same developmental age using different antisera. The same temporal age could not be used for these comparisons as many of the mutants either had their development frozen at an early stage or developed slowly. Because of the difficulty of obtaining material, and because of the impracticability of analyzing extracts from every 24 hours, when the mutants survived over 30 days, not all ages nor all antisera were studied. A complete analysis would have required many thousands of comparisons; as it was, 680 pairwise comparisons were carried out. The comparisons were classified under three headings: no difference from wild type; a quantitative difference from wild type; a qualitative difference from wild type. The results for one mutant 1(3)138 are shown in Table V.

The quantitative differences varied for each mutant and for each antiserum, showing each mutant to have a unique changing pattern of proteins during its development.

C. Drosophilin Mutants

The qualitative differences fall into two groups. The first consists of mutants in which the qualitative differences are repaired at a later stage during development. In the second group of mutants, the qualitative difference remains until death. These two groups can be illustrated with reference to one serum protein. This protein is the *Drosophila* equivalent of calliphorin (Munn and Greville, 1969; Roberts, 1971); I call it drosophilin. Drosophilin is first detected in late second-instar larvae and is present in extracts of 72-hour-old wild type. In four of the mutants, all third-instar larvae by external morphology, drosophilin cannot be detected at 96 hours. In each of these mutants, however, the protein was synthesized within the next 24 hours. While external morphological development appears to be normal, the development of the proteins of the larval serum is abnormal, the drosophilin being synthesized 24–48 hours later than in wild type. In the mutant 1(3)138, on the other hand, drosophilin is not detected in third-instar larvae at any age, although the mutant lives for at least 21 days as a third-instar larva.

D. Other Protein Mutants

In addition to 1(3)138, there are three other mutants, each of which lacks, at the time of death, one of the proteins that can be detected in wild type of the same developmental age. In each case it is a different protein.

TABLE V

A COMPARISON OF THE ANTIGEN PATTERN OF WILD TYPE AND MUTANT 1(3)138

Developmental stage	Age in hours	Serum[a]															
		G1	G4	G5	G6	G7	K1	505	507	508	511	515	516	517	521	523	524
Second instar	72	X	X	X	O	X	X	X	X	O	X	O	X	O	O	O	X
Young third instar	120	I	O	X	O	I	X	O	X	I	I	O	I	O	I	X	X
	240	I	O	O	O	I	X	O	X	X	I	O	I	O	I	X	X
	408	I	X	X	O	I	X	O	X	X	I	O	I	O	I	X	X

[a] X, same as wild type; O, quantitative difference; I, qualitative difference. G1, anti-larval serum; G4, anti-salivary glands; G5, anti-imaginal discs; G6, anti-Malpighian tubules; G7, anti-fat body; K1, anti-embryos; 505, anti-first instar; 507, anti-unfertilized egg; 508, anti-fly; 511, anti-larval serum; 515, anti-*Drosophila* chromatin; 516, anti-absorbed fly; 517, anti-ammonium sulfate fraction of egg; 521, anti-nuclear sap; 523, anti-fly (urea extract); 524, anti-Gm3 cell line.

These results show that it is possible to select mutants in which the pattern of proteins appearing at different times during development is disturbed, and it is also possible to select mutants in which a single protein is missing.

Only 16 new proteins are found in extracts of developmental stages after the stage at which the red Malpighian tubules are detected (Table II). If we assume that the proteins present before this stage are necessary for the survival of the organism, then our selected mutants can only lack one or more of these sixteen proteins, for the absence of any other protein would lead to death before the mutants could have been selected, i.e., before the red pheonotype was apparent. Considering the large number of proteins in *Drosophila*, it is very surprising that, of the 22 mutants studied, 4 should lack one of the sixteen proteins we can detect.

E. An Explanation for the Absence of Proteins

The explanation for this surprising observation is probably a simple one, that the mutation arrests development either before the cells are competent to synthesize the proteins or before the signal for the synthesis of the protein is given. However, it cannot be quite this simple for, if it were, all or many of the late proteins would be missing from all these mutants. As this does not happen, we must assume that each of these proteins is a terminal or near-terminal step in a separate developmental pathway and that the primary mutation has affected a different pathway in each of the four cases. As an example of these separate developmental pathways, we have only to think of the apparently normal development of the external morphology of the larvae (one developmental pathway) and the abnormal development of the larval serum proteins (a second developmental pathway) in the mutant 1(3)138.

In rare cases, however, the lack of protein may be due to mutations either affecting the structural gene for that protein or the immediate control of the synthesis of that protein. This class of mutant is of greatest immediate interest, for this is the class of mutant in which we can study the effect on development of the removal of a single known protein. We are currently mapping the four mutants that lack a protein and at the same time looking for electrophoretic variants of those proteins in wild-type stocks in order to map the structural gene. Coincidence of the two map positions would suggest a mutation affecting the structural gene.

F. Quantitative Differences

The four mutants showing qualitative differences also show quantitative differences. It is likely that if more of the late-appearing proteins, other than the sixteen studied here, were detected, then the mutants now showing only quantitative differences would also show qualitative differences. However, in at least two of these mutants the quantitative differences diminish as time passes, until at death the normal wild-type pattern of proteins is restored. In these two cases either we cannot detect the proteins of the affected developmental pathway or it may be that development has not been completely arrested but that the different developmental pathways have become asynchronous and that, while synchrony is achieved in the end, the trauma of this abnormal development leads to death. It is interesting to note that, in the case of both these mutants, development progresses until the late pupal period.

G. Causal Relationships

While it is possible to speculate about the significance of these changes in antigen pattern in order to understand the role played by these proteins in development it is necessary to associate specific changes with a particular developmental lesion and to establish a causal relationship between the two. To do this a detailed examination of the mutants is necessary. This examination is under way. In a preliminary study of the anatomy of the mutant larvae the mutant $I(3)138$ was shown to have abnormal imaginal discs. It is not surprising to find that imaginal discs are affected in these late lethal mutants (Shearn *et al.*, 1971; Stewart *et al.*, 1972; Shearn, 1974). However, it does not appear that there is any simple relationship between disc abnormalities and the absence of drosophilin in this mutant as other mutants with abnormal discs possess drosophilin.

VI. Control of Protein Synthesis in *Drosophila*

Currently the most intriguing molecular aspect of developmental biology is what controls the synthesis of the molecules, which in their turn influence the development of the organism. This control can be exercised at many different levels. As was suggested in the previous section, the synthesis of a protein may be the terminal event in a developmental pathway; the trigger which initiates the synthesis of this protein will work only if the cells are competent to respond. For example, whereas insect hormones are known to trigger gene activity in the salivary gland (Ashburner, 1972; Berendes, 1972), the same hormone is unlikely to trigger the same gene activity in fat-body cells. The salivary glands have the developmental competence to respond to the hormone in one way; the fat-body cells, the competence to respond in another way.

The competence of the cell is its past history, which is reflected in the array of molecules snythesized by the cell. If we know how a cell with a certain array of molecules, i.e., competence, responds to a trigger than we know how all cells with that competence will respond. The changing pattern of proteins, discussed in the previous section, reflects the changing competence of the cells. Here it is my intention to discuss the immediate response of cells to a trigger rather than to discuss the control of competence which permits that response.

A. Transcriptional and Posttranscriptional Control

The control of protein synthesis can either be at the level of transcription or be a posttranscriptional event. From our studies on *Drosophila* it is evident that both occur. Proteins not detected in unfertilized eggs are found in newly fertilized eggs before RNA synthesis begins, suggesting a posttranscriptional control of maternal mRNA (Roberts, 1971). These results are being reexamined with more detailed experiments (G. Graziosi and D. B. Roberts unpublished results), which have confirmed the earlier findings and are designed to investigate the possibility of the new proteins being released from some insoluble complex at fertilization rather than being newly synthesized.

On the other hand, using the inhibitor of mRNA synthesis actinomycin D, drosophilin was shown to be controlled at the level of transcription (Roberts, 1971).

B. The Effect of Hormones on Protein Synthesis in Cultured Cells

In order to study the control of synthesis of the proteins we are able to detect with these techniques, we turned to the simplest of our systems, cultured cells. We examined the effect of two insect hormones, the juvenile hormone mimic farnesyl methyl ether and ecdysterone, on the proteins synthesized by the cells. These hormones are known to affect gene activity in *Drosophila* (Bryant and Sang, 1965; Ashburner, 1970; Chihara *et al.*, 1972; Madhavan, 1973) and to affect cultured cells (Courgeon, 1972a,b). We expected two simple responses: (1) that the cells would synthesize proteins not previously detected in the cells, the hormone acting as an external inducer; and (2) that the synthesis of some proteins by the cell would cease, the hormone acting as an external repressor. In addition, we expected the more complicated quantitative response, which we did not intend to study in detail at this stage. All three responses were found (Moir, 1974; Moir and Roberts, 1975).

After treatment with hormone, cells were incubated in medium containing hormone and methionine-^{35}S. Extracts of these cells were compared, on immunoelectrophoresis plates, with extracts of untreated cells also grown in labeled medium. Autoradiographs were taken of the plates. Comparison of the experimental and control plates and of their autoradiographs showed which proteins were not synthesized after hormone treatment and which new proteins were synthesized. The results of one experiment with one concentration of farnesyl methyl ether and of an experiment with one concentration of ecdysterone are shown in Table VI.

TABLE VI

CHANGES IN THE PROTEINS OF CELL LINES
IN RESPONSE TO HORMONES

Time of incubation with hormone (hours)	Proteins[a]
(a) Cell line L1 treated with 0.01 µg of farnesyl methyl ether	
Control	xxxxxxxxxxxxxxxxxx
24	xx xx x
48	xxxxxxxx xxx xx x*
72	xx xx x x xxxxx xx
96	xx xx x x xx x x x
(b) Cell line Gml treated with 0.006 µg/ml ecdysterone	
Control	xxxxxxxxxxxxxxxxxxxxx
3	x xx xx x xx
6	xxxx xx x xx **
24	xx xxxxx x xxxxxxxxxxx*
48	xx xx xx x xxxxxxxxxxxxx*
72	x xx x x xxx xx xxxx

[a] x indicates the presence of a protein. * indicates a new protein.

Figure 4 shows a stained immunoelectrophoresis plate of an extract treated with hormones and a control extract and the autoradiograph of this plate.

In all, six new proteins were found after treatment with the hormones. Only three cell lines were studied, and each responded differently, reflecting their different states of competence. If all the cell lines were studied, then undoubtedly more new proteins would be found.

The immediate short-term response of all cells to farnesyl methyl ether was a reduction in protein synthesis. This was not a general effect on all proteins. The synthesis of a few proteins continued in spite of the presence of hormone, and as time passed the resynthesis of many of the proteins took place either owing to the cells adapting to the presence of the hormone or, more likely, to the hormone being metabolized. It is worth noting that the hormone had less effect on cell proteins than on organism proteins. This is what would be expected if hormones do play a major role in the control of gene activity during development.

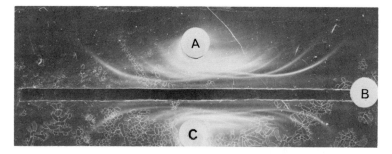

Fig. 4a. Immunoelectrophoresis plate stained with Amido schwarz 10B.

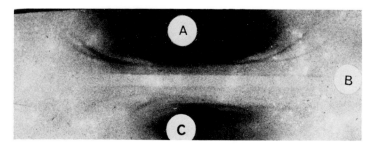

Fig. 4b. Autoradiograph Fig. 4a. A, Gm³ cell extract labeled with methionine-³⁵S; B, anti-Gm3 cell extract; C, cell extract of Gm3 cells grown for 6 hours in the presence of farnesyl methyl ether and labeled with methionine-³⁵S.

The structural genes for cell proteins would be active all the time, the hormone playing only a modulating role, while the influence of the hormone on the organism proteins, which change during development, would be much greater. The synthesis of these proteins would be switched on or off by the hormones, depending on the developmental competence of the cells.

The response to ecdysterone was more complicated; there was an initial stimulation of protein synthesis, then a decrease that reached its lowest value at 24 hours and was followed by a second stimulation, which reached its maximum after 48 hours. The increases in protein synthesis were not general, as can be seen from Table VI, which shows that some proteins are completely inhibited by this hormone.

These results demonstrate, in a different system, that insect hormones do control gene activity in the way suggested by other studies and offer a system that is easier to handle than the whole organism and can be used to study the influence of any external stimulus on gene activity. With the use of cell lines derived from stocks carrying appropriate mutants, it may be possible to use these techniques to investigate the mechanism of hormone action and gene control.

TABLE VII

Protein Changes in Cells during Development

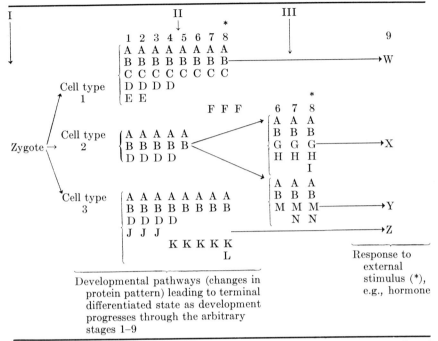

Developmental pathways (changes in protein pattern) leading to terminal differentiated state as development progresses through the arbitrary stages 1–9

Response to external stimulus (*), e.g., hormone

---

a The letters represent proteins present in the different cell types. Sequestration of proteins by one cell type which were synthesized elsewhere is ignored, as are the important quantitative changes. (1) The zygote differentiates into three cell types. (2) J is synthesized only from maternal mRNA. (3) J inhibits the synthesis of K in type 3 cells, but the dilution of J permits the synthesis of K. (4) K is diffusible and inhibits the synthesis of D in all cells. (5) ABC in type 1 cells induces the synthesis of G and H in adjacent cells of the type AB. (6) ABK in type 3 cells induces the synthesis of M in adjacent cells of the type AB. (7) ABGH induces the synthesis of F in ABC, and N in ABM. (8) ABCF induces the synthesis of L in ABK and I in ABGH. (9) Mutations affecting the establishment of the competent state ABCF prevent the synthesis of W; ABGHI, the synthesis of X; ABMN, the synthesis of Y; and ABKL, the synthesis of Z. (10) Mutations affecting ABCDEJ would be early lethals; mutations affecting the remainder, late lethals. (11) A and B are cell proteins; the remainder, organism proteins. (12) These results, representing all cell types together, can be displayed in a form that is a simplification of the upper part of Table II:

Developmental stage	Presence of Antigen
1	xxxxxx
2	xxxxxx
3	xxxxx
4	xxxxx
5	xxxx
6	xxxxxxx
7	xxxxxxxxx
8	xxxxxxxxxx
9	xxxxxxxxxxxxxx

VII. Summary and Conclusions

These results demonstrate three major points:

1. The proteins of *Drosophila* change during development and are different in different tissues or cells.

2. Mutations affecting the development of *Drosophila* frequently [invariably (?) if more proteins were studied] lead to the absence of a protein.

3. Different cell lines respond in a different way to such external stimuli as hormones.

These points are summarized in Table VII. This scheme pinpoints the three most important areas for study: (1) What establishes the initial differences between the cell types (I)? (2) How do the protein molecules interact to give the variety of cell types in the organism (II)? (3) How is the expression of a single gene controlled (III)?

Three hypotheses have been proposed to account for the initial differences in the cell types: (1) the unequal segregation of molecules in the unfertilized egg; (2) Gradients; and (3) the position of the cell in the embryo. To investigate whether one or more of these account for the initial differences in the *Drosophila* embryo requires detailed analysis of early development, especially of the distribution of proteins in the unfertilzed egg.

How the molecules interact to give rise to the variety of cell types might be investigated by analyzing the mutants in which one of these molecules is missing, as described above.

Finally, the immediate control of gene activity in response to an external stimulus can be investigated either by a study of mutants which fail to respond to that stimulus, e.g., puff mutants (Ashburner *et al.*, 1973), or by selecting mutants of cultured cells which fail to respond.

ACKNOWLEDGMENT

I would like to thank my colleagues Susan Moffitt, Anne Moir, Guida Boavida, Peter Andrews, and Giorgio Graziosi for their collaboration in this work, my stock-keeper Nancy Rudden, and Mrs. Jean Matthews who kept us all supplied with medium. This work was supported by grants from the Science Research Council and the Cancer Research Campaign.

REFERENCES

Andrews, P. W., and Roberts, D. B. (1974). *Nucl. Acids Res.* **1**, 979.
Ashburner, M. (1970a). *Advan. Insect Physiol.* **7**, 1.
Ashburner, M. (1970b). *Nature (London)* **227**, 187.
Ashburner, M. (1972). *In* "Developmental Studies on Giant Chromosomes" (W. Beerman, ed.), p. 101. Springer-Verlag, Berlin and New York.

Ashburner, M., Chihara, C., Meltzer, P., and Richards, G. (1973). *Cold Spring Harbor Symp. Quant. Biol.* **38**, 655.
Berendes, H. D. (1972). *In* "Developmental Studies on Giant Chromosomes" (W. Beerman, ed.), p. 181. Springer-Verlag, Berlin and New York.
Bishop, J. O., Morton, J. G., Rosbash, M., and Richardson, M. (1974). *Nature (London)* **250**, 199.
Boavida, M. G. (1973). Ph.D. Thesis, Leeds University.
Boavida, M. G., and Roberts, D. B. (1975). *J. Insect Physiol.* (in press).
Bodenstein, D. (1950). *In* "Biology of *Drosophila*" (M. Demerec, ed.), p. 675. Wiley, New York.
Brachet, J. (1960). *In* "The Biochemistry of Development," p. 257. Pergamon, Oxford.
Brewer, G. J. (1970). "An Introduction to Isozyme Techniques." Academic Press, New York.
Bryant, P., and Sang, J. H. (1968). *Nature (London)* **220**, 393.
Chihara, C. J., Petri, W. H., Fristrom, J. W., and King, D. S. (1972). *J. Insect Physiol.* **18**, 1115.
Courgeon, A. M. (1972a). *Exp. Cell Res.* **74**, 327.
Courgeon, A. M. (1972b). *Nature (London), New Biol.* **238**, 250.
Doane, W. W. (1973). *In* "Development Systems: Insects" (S. J. Counce and C. H. Waddington, eds.), Vol. 2, p. 291. Academic Press, New York.
Echalier, G., and Ohanessian, A. (1970). *In Vitro* **6**, 162.
Ephrussi, B. (1972). *In* "Hybridization of Somatic Cells." p. 53. Princeton Univ. Press, Princeton, New Jersey.
Hadorn, E. (1961). "Developmental Genetics and Lethal Factors." Methuen, London.
Holtzer, H., and Abbot, J. (1968). *In* "The Stability of the Differentiated State" (H. Urspring, ed.), p. 1. Springer-Verlag, Berlin and New York.
Judd, B. H., Shen, M. W., and Kaufman, T. C. (1972). *Genetics* **71**, 139.
Lindsley, D. L., and Grell, E. H. (1968). *Carnegie Inst. Wash. Publ.* **627**.
Madhavan, K. (1973). *J. Insect Physiol.* **19**, 441.
Moir, A. (1974). Ph.D. Thesis, Oxford University.
Moir, A., and Roberts, D. B. (1975). In preparation.
Mosna, G., and Dolfini, S. (1972). *Chromosoma* **38**, 1.
Munn, E. A., and Greville, G. D. (1969). *J. Insect Physiol.* **15**, 1935.
Pasteur, N., and Kastritsis, C. D. (1971). *Develop. Biol.* **26**, 525.
Patel, N. G., and Schneiderman, H. A. (1969). *J. Insect Physiol.* **15**, 643.
Poulson, D. F. (1950). *In* "Biology of Drosophila" (M. Demerec, ed.), p. 168. Wiley, New York.
Ripoll, P., and Garcia-Bellido, A. (1973). *Nature (London), New Biol.* **241**, 15.
Roberts, D. B. (1971). *Nature (London)* **233**, 394.
Roberts, D. B., and Andrews, P. W. (1975). In preparation.
Roberts, D. B., and Pateman, J. A. (1964). *J. Gen. Microbiol.* **34**, 295.
Schneider, I. (1972). *J. Embryol. Exp. Morphol.* **27**, 353.
Shearn, A. (1974). *Genetics* **77**, 115.
Shearn, A., Rice, T., Garen, A., and Gehring, W. (1971). *Proc. Nat. Acad. Sci. U.S.* **68**, 2594.
Sonnenblick, B. P. (1950). *In* "Biology of *Drosophila*" (M. Demerec, ed.), p. 62. Wiley, New York.
Stewart, M., Murphy, C., and Fristrom, J. W. (1972). *Develop. Biol.* **27**, 71.
Wright, T. R. F. (1970). *Advan. Genet.* **15**, 262.

SUBJECT INDEX